TWENTIETH CENTURY DISCOVERY

Some other Doubleday science books by Isaac Asimov

LIFE AND ENERGY

A SHORT HISTORY OF BIOLOGY

A SHORT HISTORY OF CHEMISTRY

THE NEUTRINO

TWENTIETH CENTURY DISCOVERY

BY ISAAC ASIMOV

xx

DOUBLEDAY & COMPANY, INC.,   GARDEN CITY, NEW YORK

To Liz, Meg, Marion, and Diane

Who show that beauty and brains do, too, mix.

CONTENTS

INTRODUCTION

We are living in a hurry-up world, and it's getting more hurry-up all the time. We are making more new discoveries now than we ever have before, and we will make still more in the future.

The result is that the kind of world a youngster is learning to live in now is quite different from the world he will have to live in when he is grown up and has youngsters of his own.

It was not always this way. Many thousands of years ago, men did not have the fine cities of today and the complicated machinery we use. They lived in caves or in simple huts, dressed in animal skins, ate nuts, berries, and fruit, together with the animals they could find and kill with stone axes or stone-tipped arrows.

Every once in a while, some man, or group of men, made a great discovery. There was no way of spreading the knowledge except by one person telling another. They might not even do that because they might want to keep the discovery secret. For that reason, it would take a very long time for a new discovery to become known to all mankind.

Man's first great discovery seems to have been to learn how to start a fire. We don't know when that took place or how long the knowledge took to spread.

We do know, though, about a later discovery. Perhaps ten or eleven thousand years ago, groups of men and women in southwestern Asia first learned how to grow plants for food. They had discovered farming, or agriculture. Much more food was produced by farming than just by hunting and gathering. Wherever men farmed, the population grew larger, cities were built, and civilizations were developed.

But it took as much as 5,000 years for this very useful discovery to spread from western Asia to Western Europe.

Then, about 3,500 years ago, groups of men in southwestern Asia (very near where agriculture had started) learned how to extract iron out of iron ore. The iron could be used to make tools and war weapons that were much better than those that already existed.

This time it took not quite 1,000 years for the discovery to spread from western Asia to Western Europe.

Why did it travel more quickly this time? You see, as civilization grew and spread, it became easier and easier for one man to tell his knowledge to another. Men learned how to write and could prepare books of instructions. They could establish schools.

As the population grew, there came to be more and more men thinking about various problems and trying to work out solutions. Important discoveries began to come more frequently and each spread a little more quickly than the one before. Changes in ways of living began to hurry up a bit.

Even so, until about 1750, change took place so slowly that a particular person didn't see much of it in his own lifetime. If he were a farmer or a goldsmith or a sailor, he did his work just about the way his father and grandfather did. He lived in the same kind of house, ate the same kind of food, believed the same kind of beliefs.

But then, not long after 1750, mankind reached a turning point. A Scotsman, James Watt, designed a very useful steam engine. In such a steam engine, water is boiled over a fire of burning wood or coal and steam is formed. The steam is kept in a closed chamber, but pushes outward in all directions. This push builds up till there is enough force to move a piston which turns a wheel which makes machinery go.

For the first time, man could do work by using the energy in burning coal instead of the energy of his own muscles or the muscles of animals. Not only could burning coal do far more work far more quickly than human muscles could—but more and more human beings were freed from hard labor so that they could spend their time thinking.

This change came to be called the "Industrial Revolution" and it spread rapidly. In a hundred years, it had reached over all of Western Europe and into the United States. In another hundred years, it had changed Russia and Japan into modern nations and was reaching into most of the rest of the world.

Population grew more rapidly and discoveries and inventions came faster and faster. Now things are no longer changing after thousands of years or even after hundreds, but after merely tens of years.

Think of the changes that have taken place since World War II ended less than thirty years ago. There was no television then and no jet planes. Now there are few American homes without large television sets, many in color, and thousands of people are "jetting" all over the world.

There were no giant computers then, no antibiotics, no tranquilizers. Nothing had ever been shot off the Earth into orbit.

Now diseases have been conquered, mechanical organs have been placed in human bodies and organs have been transplanted from one human being to another. In the poorer parts of the world the average person is living twice as long as he had a chance of living just thirty years ago.

Hundreds of satellites have been orbited. Objects have been hurled past the moon, Venus, and Mars. Men have remained in outer space for weeks.

Life has changed in little ways, too. Large-scale freezing has become a great way of making it possible for us to eat all kinds of food all year round. Big department stores are everywhere; as are drive-in movies and electric toothbrushes.

So hurry-up is the world now that it has become a confusing place indeed. No one can follow all the changes; no one can grasp them all.

Yet we would want to follow them as much as possible. Partly this would be out of curiosity. This search into the puzzles of the universe is interesting and exciting and the new knowledge and discoveries that come out of it make our lives different.

Then, too, if we understand the new discoveries that are leading to changes, we may be better prepared for the changes that will come with still newer discoveries not yet made.

Of course, it is impossible in a single book to describe *all* the new discoveries that have been made in the twentieth century. Only a few can be considered, and I have chosen some that I believe to be of interest and importance to tell you about in the pages that follow.

TWENTIETH CENTURY DISCOVERY

1—WAR AGAINST THE SIX-LEGS

Just about the greatest problem we all face now is our own numbers. We crowd the earth more thickly now than we ever have before and this is creating strains.

Before the invention of agriculture about 8500 B.C., man lived on the animals he could catch and kill and on the plants he could find that were good to eat. At that time, there weren't many human beings on Earth. One careful guess is that there were only eight million people on the whole planet. (That's about the population of New York City today. Imagine New Yorkers being the only people alive and that they were spread over the entire planet.)

The reason there were so few then was that there are only so many animals to be caught and only so many plants to be found. If, for some reason, there were suddenly more people, some of them would be sure to starve to death. The population would shrink again.

Once agriculture was developed, people deliberately grew large quantities of plants that could be eaten. There was more food to be found in one spot and more people could eat well. Population increased.

By the time of Julius Caesar, in 50 B.C., there were fifty million people living on agriculture around the shores of the

Mediterranean Sea. Another fifty million were living in China and another fifty million in the rest of the world. The total for the world was 150 million but that was still less than the population of the United States alone today.

Population continued to increase and by 1600 A.D., it had reached 500 million.

After that, the increase became so rapid that we can speak of a "population explosion." New continents had been discovered with large tracts of land into which people could push and where they could begin to farm. The Industrial Revolution came and made it possible to farm more efficiently and ship food greater distances.

By 1800, the world population was 900 million; by 1900, it was 1,600,000,000. Now, it is about 3,500,000,000. Three and a half billion people are alive today.

In recent years, medical advances have placed many diseases under control. The death rate has dropped and with fewer people dying, population is increasing faster than ever. The world population doubled between 1900 and 1969, a period of sixty-nine years. It will double again, in all likelihood, between 1969 and 2009, a period of only forty years.

When the twenty-first century opens, and the youngsters of today are in middle life and raising a family, the world population will be something like 6,500,000,000. The United States alone will have a population of 330 million.

Naturally, this can't continue forever. There comes a point when the number of men, women, and children is too great to feed and take care of. If the numbers become too great, there will be famine and disease. Desperate, hungry men will fight and there will be wars and revolts.

With this in mind, many people are trying to discover ways of limiting the population by controlling the number of births. It seems to make sense that no more children should be born than we can feed and take care of. It is no act of kindness to bring a child into the world who must starve, or live a miserable, stunted life.

It is possible that kind and intelligent ways of controlling birth will be accepted and that human population will reach some reasonable level and stay there. It will take time for this to come to pass, however, and no matter what we do the figure of 6,500,000,000 will probably be reached. Even if it goes no higher, we will have to count on feeding and taking care of this number.

This will be difficult. At this very time, when the world population is only 3,500,000,000, we are having difficulty. Large sections of the world are poorly fed. There are perhaps 300 million children in the world who are so badly underfed that they may have suffered permanent brain damage and will therefore never be quite as intelligent and useful as they might have been if they had only received proper food. Nations such as India face famine and would have seen millions die already if it were not that the United States shipped them huge quantities of grain out of its own plentiful supplies. But American supplies are dwindling fast, and when they are gone, what will happen to nations like India?

There are no longer large empty spaces of good land which farmers can utilize. The fertile areas of the world are all in use. We have to try to find less easy solutions. We can bring water to dry areas. We can use chemicals to restore the fertility of soil which has been fading out after centuries of farming. We can use more fish from the ocean; and perhaps we can even grow plants in the sea.

Actually, mankind has been steadily increasing food production since World War II. The trouble is that this food increase has barely matched the population increase. Despite all the extra food, each individual today gets no more than he used to get twenty years ago. The percentage of hungry people in the world stays the same.

And as the population rises ever faster, it is important that the food supply increase ever faster also. It is important to feed the ever-increasing numbers of human beings until such time as the population can come under control.

One way of doing so, without having to increase the size of our farmlands one bit, would be to prevent any of our precious food from being eaten by creatures other than humans. Farmers are always on the watch for hawks that eat their chickens, coyotes that eat their lambs, crows that eat their corn.

These are creatures we can see and do something about. We can lay traps, or shoot, or set up scarecrows.

But hawks, and coyotes, and crows are nothing at all compared to an enemy that is much smaller, much more dangerous, and until very recently, almost impossible to fight.

These are the insects; the little buzzing, flying six-legged creatures that we find everywhere.

Insects are the most successful form of animal life on earth. There are nearly a million different kinds (or "species") of insects known, and perhaps another two million species exist that have not yet been discovered and described. This is far more than the total number of different species of all other animals put together.

The number of individual insects is incredible. In and above a single acre of moist soil there may be as many as four million insects of hundreds of different species. There may be as many as a billion billion (1,000,000,000,000,000,000) insects living in the world right now—over 300 million insects for each man, woman, and child alive.

Almost all the different species of insects are harmless to man. They are, indeed, useful in the scheme of life. Many insects serve as the food supply for the pleasant songbirds we all enjoy. Other insects help pollinate plants, and without that the plants would die.

Some insects are directly useful to man. The bee produces honey and wax, the silkworm produces silk, and certain scale insects produce a brilliant red dye. Some insects, such as locusts, are even eaten by men in some areas of the world.

To be sure, there are some species of insects that are troublesome. Perhaps 3,000 species at most (out of a possible three million) are nuisances. These include the mosquitoes, flies, fleas, lice, wasps, hornets, weevils, cockroaches, carpet beetles, and so on.

As a result, people come to dislike "bugs" and get the urge to swat or crush anything with six legs that flies or crawls. This is wrong, though. We don't want really to wipe out all insects because a few are bothersome. Insects, as I said, are necessary to the scheme of life.

In fact, all the different species of creatures are useful to each other. Even killer animals are useful to the creatures they kill.

As an example, mountain lions kill deer. Now deer are pretty animals while mountain lions seem to be dangerous killers that deserve to be wiped out. It has happened that men have killed the mountain lions in some areas and freed the deer from the danger.

That does not do the deer a favor!

While the mountain lions were active they killed some deer but never very many. What's more, they usually killed old or sick deer, for the strong young ones had a better chance to get away. The mountain lions kept the numbers of deer down and there was that much more food for those that were left.

Once the mountain lions were gone, the deer population increased quickly. Even the old and sick had a chance to live. All the deer searched the countryside for food and in no time the area was stripped bare. Starvation gripped the herd and all became weak and sick. They began to die and in the end there were far fewer deer than there had been in the days when the mountain lions were active.

So you see, the deer depend for their life and health on the very animals that seem to be killing them.

The way in which different species of animals depend upon one another results in a "balance of nature." The numbers of any particular species stay about the same for long periods of time because of this balance. Even if the balance is temporarily upset, when one species grows unusually numerous or unusually rare, the food supplies drop, or increase, in such a way that the proper number is restored.

The study of this balance of nature is called "ecology" and it has grown to be one of the branches of science that is of greatest interest to mankind, for we have badly upset the balance of nature and are upsetting it worse each year.

In the end, we might suffer as the deer suffer when the mountain lions are gone, and scientists are anxious to prevent this if possible. By studying the principles of ecology, they hope to learn how best to prevent it.

Actually, insects wouldn't have grown to be such nuisances, if mankind hadn't upset the balance of nature many thousands of years ago when he first developed agriculture. Once he began to plant barley, for instance, he saw to it that many acres of land produced hardly anything but barley, barley, barley. All the other plants that might have been growing on those acres he wiped out as much as possible. They were "weeds."

Animals that lived on those weeds were starved out. On the other hand, animals that lived on barley multiplied, for suddenly they had a huge food supply.

In this way, agriculture encouraged certain insects to multiply and what had been just a nuisance became a great danger. As an example, locusts may suddenly multiply and swarm down on fields in gigantic armies of billions. This happened frequently in ancient times and even the Bible describes such a locust plague in the book of Joel. Locusts would sweep across the fields, eating everything green. When they left, a barren waste would remain.

This would be a disaster, for large numbers of people would

be depending upon those vanished crops. Widespread famine would be the result.

Nor could anything be done about it. People were completely helpless as they watched their food disappear. They might go out and try to kill locusts, but no matter how hard they worked at it, there would be ten thousand left alive for every one they killed.

Even today, although scientists have discovered ways of fighting insects, there is serious trouble in some places and at some times. This is especially true in the less-developed countries where scientific methods of fighting insects are least available—and where the population can least afford the loss.

In India, for instance, there is an insect called the "red cotton bug" which lives on the cotton plant. If cotton plants were growing wild, some of them might be affected by the bug, but the plants would be few in number and would be spread widely apart. The bugs would not have much to eat and would find it difficult to get from one plant to the other. The number of red cotton bugs would therefore remain small and the cotton plants themselves would be only slightly damaged. They would continue to grow quite well.

In large cotton fields, however, the bugs have a tremendous food supply, with one plant right on top of the other. The bugs increase in numbers, therefore, and become a huge horde. Each year, half of all the cotton grown in India is destroyed by them.

Even in the United States, we have trouble. An insect called the "boll weevil" feeds on the cotton plant in this country. We can fight the boll weevil better than the Indians can fight the cotton bug. Still, as a result of the boll weevil damage, each pound of cotton produced in the United States costs ten cents more than it would if the boll weevil didn't exist.

The losses resulting from insect damage in the United States alone run to something like eight billion dollars each year.

Man himself has also vastly increased in numbers since

agriculture was developed. Before that, small groups of men hunted through wide stretches of forests. They offered only a small target for fleas and lice.

After the appearance of agriculture, farming communities were established. These were much larger than hunting bands, and in such communities, men lived huddled together. Fleas and lice multiplied and men had to do a great deal more scratching. Mosquitoes, too, gained a much larger food supply and increased in numbers.

You might think that insects like termites and boll weevils did real damage and that fleas and lice were just nuisances, but that is wrong. The insects that bite and sting human beings can be terrible dangers; and this was something that wasn't discovered until the opening of the twentieth century.

The discovery came in connection with yellow fever. This is a rapidly spreading disease that can kill vast numbers of people. Nowadays it is rarely heard of in the United States but in previous centuries, it would suddenly flare up in huge epidemics that would lay whole cities low. Twenty times in the history of the city of Philadelphia, yellow fever epidemics raged across it. New York had fifteen epidemics.

There seemed no way of preventing the epidemics. They struck out of nowhere and suddenly people were dying on every side. The United States military forces grew particularly interested in the problem in 1898.

In that year we fought a short war with Spain. Most of the fighting took place in Cuba where few Americans were killed by Spanish guns, but many died of yellow fever. What people didn't understand was how the yellow fever passed from one person to another. Was it by infected clothing, by polluted water, or how?

In 1899, the American government sent to Cuba a team of doctors headed by Walter Reed. Their mission was to find out how yellow fever was spread. Yellow fever does not attack animals so the mission had to work with human beings, and that meant using themselves as guinea pigs.

They handled the clothing and bedding of people sick with yellow fever yet didn't come down with it themselves. Walter Reed remembered that a few people had advanced the notion some years before that mosquitoes might carry the disease. They would bite sick men and suck in infected blood, then pass the infection to the next person they bit.

Reed's group checked this. They introduced mosquito netting to keep mosquitoes away from certain houses. Sure enough, they found that people protected by mosquito netting usually didn't get the disease even when it was striking all around.

They went on to something more daring. They captured mosquitoes in rooms where there were men sick with yellow fever and then allowed those mosquitoes to bite them. Some of the group soon came down with yellow fever and one of them, Jesse William Lazear, died.

A mosquito bite is more than a nuisance, then. Mosquitoes of a certain species can pass on a deadly disease with their bite.

Yellow fever struck the United States again, for the last time, in 1904, with New Orleans the victim. But Reed had shown how to fight the disease. The mosquitoes were kept away with netting. The places where they bred were wiped out. As a result, yellow fever is no longer a serious danger in the United States. There hasn't been an epidemic in this country in over sixty years.

Another species of mosquito was found to spread the disease called malaria. Malaria isn't as dramatic as yellow fever. It isn't as rapid a killer. Besides, there is a drug, quinine (obtained from the bark of a South American tree), that, for centuries now, has been known to control the disease.

Even so, malaria is the most widespread disease in the world—or it was. As late as 1955, there were estimated to be no less than 250 million people in the world who were sick of malaria. Each year 2,500,000 people died of it. Those who didn't die were greatly weakened and couldn't work as healthy people could. Entire nations were greatly reduced in vigor and in the ability to help themselves because so many individuals among them were malarial. And all the result of mosquito bites.

Certain species of insects in Africa, called the "tsetse fly," spread sleeping sickness, a brain infection that usually ends in death. This disease spread into eastern Africa at the beginning of the twentieth century and between 1901 and 1906 it killed 200,000 people in Uganda. About two out of every three people in the affected areas died.

The disease also affects horses and cattle. It is the tsetse fly more than anything else—more than the heat, the jungle, or the large wild animals—that keeps sections of Africa from advancing.

Naturally, men were anxious to kill insects. Insects were starving mankind, eating his grain and fruits and fibers, too. Insects were killing men with their infected bites. Men *had* to strike back.

One way was to poison insects. Suppose, for instance, you sprayed your crops with a solution of "Paris green," a deadly poison compound containing copper and arsenic.

Paris green did not affect the plants. The plants lived on carbon dioxide in the air and on certain minerals which they absorbed from the soil. If there was some poison on their leaves, that made no difference.

Any insect trying to feed on the leaves that were coated with Paris green would, however, die at once. Insects simply could not live on sprayed plants and the plants grew large and ripe without being bothered. Paris green was an "insecticide," a word meaning "insect-killer."

(Nowadays, the word is used less often because insects are

not the only kind of creature we want to kill. There are also worms and snails, mice and rats, even rabbits—all of which become serious problems if they grow too numerous. They are all lumped together as "pests" and any chemical used to kill any of them is a "pesticide." In this chapter, though, I will be talking chiefly about insects and I will continue to use the word insecticide.)

Paris green and other mineral insecticides have their draw-backs. For one thing, they are just as poisonous to human beings as they are to insects. Foods which have been sprayed with these solutions must be carefully washed, or they could be deadly.

And, of course, plants are washed, naturally, by rain. The rain tends to remove some of the mineral poison and drip it down to the soil. Little by little, the soil accumulates copper, arsenic, and other elements which will reach the roots of the plants eventually. There they do affect plants and the soil will after a while become poisonous to them.

What's more, such mineral insecticides can't be used on human beings themselves. Sometimes it would be most useful if we could use them so, to destroy insects that live directly on people.

Mosquitoes and flies may bite people and annoy them (or sometimes transmit diseases that kill them) but at least they don't actually live *on* people. If we want to attack them, we can keep them off by netting, spray the places where they land with poison, or find the stagnant pools or garbage where they breed and either remove or spray them.

But what about the fleas and lice that live in human clothing or hair? In many parts of the world even today there are no automatic washers in which clothes can be washed every couple of days. There isn't even a supply of soap or of clean running water. The poorer people have very little in the way of clothing and if there is a cold season they must simply wear the same clothes all winter long.

Naturally, the fleas and lice in that clothing have a happy hunting ground all winter long. This was all the more true if people were forced to crowd into small dirty hovels or tenements. If anyone happened not to have fleas and lice, he quickly caught them from others.

This could be extremely serious because typhus, a disease always present among the poor, every once in a while became epidemic and spread everywhere. It was most likely to be found among poor, dirty people huddled together on ships, for instance, or in jails. It was particularly dangerous during wars when many thousands of soldiers might be penned up in a besieged town or in lines of trenches or in prisoners' camps.

When thousands of Irish emigrated to America after the potato blight brought famine to Ireland in the 1840s, half of them sickened with typhus on the way here. In World War I, typhus did more damage among the miserable soldiers in eastern and southeastern Europe than the guns did.

The little country of Serbia drove back the armies of much larger Austria-Hungary several times in 1914 and 1915, but then typhus struck and crippled the small nation. The Austrians dared not invade while the epidemic was raging but afterward they marched in and what was left of the Serbian army could not stop them.

By the time of World War I, however, doctors knew very well what was causing the spread of typhus. They had learned that from a French physician, Charles Nicolle, who, in 1903, had been appointed director of a medical institute in Tunis in North Africa. (Tunis belonged to France at the time.)

Tunis was riddled with typhus but Nicolle noticed a very curious thing. The disease was infectious only outside the hospital, not inside. Doctors visiting patients in their homes caught typhus. Medical attendants who admitted patients into the hospital caught it. But once the patients were *in* the hospital, they stopped being infectious, even though they might be sicker than ever. Doctors and nurses who tended typhus patients inside the hospital never caught typhus themselves.

Nicolle decided that something happened at the moment that patients entered the hospital that changed everything. For one thing, the patient had removed the clothes he was wearing and took a bath. The clothes were gotten rid of and the infectiousness disappeared.

By that time the word was about that mosquitoes spread yellow fever and malaria, so it didn't seem hard to believe that maybe typhus fever was spread by the lice in the dirty clothes.

Nicolle worked with animals, first with chimpanzees, and then with guinea pigs, and he proved his case completely. Typhus would spread by a louse bite, not otherwise.

Nor is typhus the only disease to be spread by such body insects. There is a dreaded disease called "plague." In the fourteenth century, it spread all across Europe and killed one out of every three human beings on the continent. It was called "the Black Death" then.

This disease is spread by fleas. The fleas that are most dangerous live on rats and wherever the rats spread, so do the fleas. When a flea bites a sick rat, then jumps on a human being and bites him, it is usually all up with the human.

These are hard diseases to conquer. Rats are difficult creatures to get rid of. Even today they infest American slums and are a downright danger to sleeping babies. Body lice or fleas are even harder to eliminate.

After all you can't avoid lice and fleas by something as simple as mosquito netting. You must wash clothes and body regularly, but how can you ask people to do that who have no soap and no clean water?

It would be helpful if you could spray the bodies and clothes with insecticide, but you would have to find one that would kill the insects without killing the person. Certainly Paris green wouldn't do.

Instead of minerals, then, the search was on for some suitable organic substance. An organic substance is one that has a structure similar to the compounds contained in living tissue. There are many millions of different organic substances, and no two species of creatures act exactly alike in response to particular organic substances.

Might it not be possible to find an organic substance which would interfere with some of the chemical reactions that go on in insects, but not in other kinds of animals.

In 1935, a Swiss chemist, Paul Müller, began to search for such a compound. He wanted one that could be easily made and would therefore be cheap. It had to be without an unpleasant odor. It had to kill insects but be reasonably harmless to other kinds of life.

He narrowed down the search by studying different classes of organic compounds and then following up those classes that showed at least a little promise. He would study the chemical structure of those compounds that showed a little promise and would then try a slightly different compound to see if that had more promise. If it did, he would study the difference in structure and see how to make a still further difference that would be better still.

It took four years but in September of 1939 (the very month in which World War II started), Müller came across a compound called "dichlorodiphenyltrichloroethane." That is a long name even for chemists and it is usually referred to by its initials, as DDT. This compound had first been prepared and described in 1874 but at that time there seemed nothing unusual about it. Now, however, Müller discovered that DDT was the very thing he was looking for. It was cheap, stable, and odorless, fairly harmless to most forms of life, but meant death to insects.

By 1942, preparations containing DDT were beginning to be manufactured for sale to the public, and in 1943, it had its first dramatic use. The city of Naples, in Italy, had been captured by Allied forces and, as winter came on, typhus began to spread.

It wasn't possible to make the population strip off their clothes, burn them, and put on new clothes, so something else was done. Soldiers and civilians were lined up and sprayed with a DDT solution. The lice died and typhus died with them. For the first time in human history, a winter epidemic of typhus had been stopped in its tracks.

To show that this was no accident the same thing was done in Japan in late 1945, after the American occupation.

Since World War II, DDT and other organic insecticides have been used in large quantities. Tens of thousands of tons are produced each year. The United States alone spent over a billion dollars for such insecticides in the single year of 1966.

Not only are our crops saved but the various insect-spread diseases are all but wiped out. Since DDT wipes out mosquitoes and flies, as well as lice, malaria is now almost unknown in the United States. Less than a hundred cases a year are reported and almost all are brought in from abroad.

Yet this does not represent a happy ending. The use of organic insecticides has brought troubles in its train. Sometimes such insecticides don't work because they upset the balance of nature.

For instance, DDT might be fairly deadly to an insect we want to kill, but even more deadly to another insect that lives on the first one. Only a few harmful insects survive but their insect enemies are now all dead. In a short time, the insects we don't want are more numerous than they were before the use of DDT.

Then, too, organic insecticides don't kill *all* species of insects. Some insects have a chemical machinery that isn't affected by these poisons; they are "resistant." It may happen that a resistant insect could do damage to our crops but usually doesn't because some other insect is more numerous and gets the lion's share of the food.

If DDT kills the damaging insect, but leaves the resistant insect behind, then that resistant insect can multiply enormously. It then becomes a great danger and DDT can't touch it.

In fact, even among those species of insects that are killed by DDT there are always a few individuals that differ chemically from the rest and are resistant. They survive when all other individuals are killed. They multiply and then a whole species of resistant insects comes into existence.

Thus, as the years pass, DDT has become less effective on the house fly, for instance. Some resistance was reported as early as 1947, and this has been growing more serious. By now almost every species of insect has developed resistance, including the body louse that spreads typhus.

Finally, even though organic insecticides are not very poisonous to creatures other than insects, they are not entirely harmless either. If too much insecticide is used, some birds can be poisoned. Fish are particularly easy to kill, and if insecticides are used on water to kill young insects, young fish may also go in great numbers.

Organic insecticides are also washed into the soil. Eventually, they are broken down by bacteria but not very quickly. Some accumulates in the soil, then in the plants that grow in the soil, then in the animals that eat the plants. All animals, including man, have a little bit of DDT inside ourselves. Not enough to hurt us so far, but it is there.

For that reason, attempts have been made to control insects by means that don't involve chemicals.

For one thing, there are certain strains of plants which are naturally resistant to particular insects. These strains might be cultivated.

Then, too, crops might be rotated; one crop might be

grown one year, another crop the next. In this way, an insect which flourished one year might drop to very low levels the next when the wrong plants were grown, plants it could not eat. It would have to start from scratch again and its numbers would stay low. Or else one might break up the fields so that not too large an area would be devoted to a single crop. That would make it harder for an insect to spread.

Here's something else—insects have their enemies. The enemy might exist in one part of the world but not in another. It might be another insect or some kind of parasite. If it could be introduced in places where the insect we were after was flourishing, the numbers of that insect might be brought under control.

Modern science has worked up a number of additional devices for killing insects. Bats eat insects and locate them by emitting very shrill squeaks, squeaks too shrill for us to hear. The sound waves of these squeaks bounce off the insect, and the bat, by listening for the echo, knows where the insect is.

Naturally, insects have developed an instinctive avoidance of such a sound. If a device is set up to send out these shrill "ultrasonic" squeaks, insects stay away from a wide area near it.

Another device is just the opposite—to attract rather than to repel. Insects can find each other over large distances because they can smell each other. Female moths give off an odor that a male moth of the same species can detect many hundreds of yards away. Female moths can tell by smell a good spot on which to lay eggs.

Chemists have worked to isolate the chemicals that give off this attractive odor. Once they isolate it, they can place it on certain spots to attract insects. If those spots are sprayed with insecticide, too, insects could die in great numbers. Only a little insecticide would have to be used; it wouldn't have to be spread everywhere; and it would be less likely to affect other forms of life.

Or else a female could be induced to lay eggs in an unsuitable place by means of a sprayed odor, so that the eggs would not develop.

Then, too, male insects can be subjected to radioactivity that destroys some of their internal organs so they cannot fertilize the female's eggs. If such sterilized males are released, the females end up laying eggs that cannot develop. An insect called the "screwworm," which infests cattle in southeastern United States, was almost wiped out by this method.

But all that mankind is doing today is not yet enough. The insecticides are too poisonous and the other methods are a little too fancy for undeveloped countries where the insect menace is greatest. Is there something better we can do to help feed the doubled population of 2000?

Actually, the 1960s are seeing the development of an exciting new way of battling insects, a way that makes the insects fight themselves, so to speak. To understand how this should be, let's consider how insects grow.

An insect has two chief stages to its life. In its young form, it is a "larva"; later on, it is an "adult." The two forms are very often completely different in appearance.

Consider the caterpillar, for instance. It is a larva, a wingless, wormlike creature with stumpy little leg-like structures. Eventually, though, it becomes a moth or butterfly, with the usual six legs of the insect, and often with gorgeous wings. Similarly, the housefly develops out of its egg as a tiny, wormlike "maggot."

The reason for two such different forms is that the two have widely different specialties. The larva spends almost all its time eating and growing. It is almost what we might call an eating machine with all its makeup concentrated on that. The adult, on the other hand, is an egg-laying machine. Sometimes adult insects do nothing *but* lay eggs. Mayflies live less than a day after they reach the adult stage and don't even have proper eating apparatus. In their short adult life they just lay eggs; they don't have to eat.

The change from larva to adult is called "metamorphosis." Sometimes the metamorphosis is not a very startling one. A young grasshopper looks quite grasshopperish, for instance.

Where the metamorphosis is a thoroughgoing one, as in the case of the caterpillar, the insect must pause in its life cycle to make the enormous change within its body. It is almost as though it must go back into an original egg stage and start all over. It becomes a motionless, apparently dead object, slowly changing within and making itself over until it is ready to step forth as an adult. In this motionless intermediate stage it is called a "pupa."

There are insect species which act in such a way as to protect this defenseless pupa stage. In its final period as a larva, it will produce thin jets of liquid from special openings in its abdomen. These jets harden into a tough fiber which the larva weaves round about itself until it is completely enclosed. This is the "cocoon" within which the pupa remains hidden till metamorphosis is done. It is the fiber from the cocoon of the silkworm moth that provides mankind with silk.

All this requires careful organization. For instance, it is a problem for a larva just to grow. The larva is surrounded by a thin, but tough, cuticle made of a substance called "chitin." This protects it and gives it an anchor for its muscles, but chitin doesn't expand with the body.

As a larva grows, its cuticle becomes tighter and tighter about it. Finally, the cuticle splits and is shed. The larva is said to "molt." From the split cuticle, the larva wriggles. It is expanded now and is distinctly bigger now that the cuticle which had been holding it in like a tight girdle is gone. A new, but roomier, cuticle quickly forms and within it the larva grows again.

But what makes the cuticle split at just the right time? The answer is that there is an automatic chemical control involved. Any living creature is a complex setup of automatic self-regulating chemical machinery. This is true even of the human being and it was only at the very opening of the twentieth century that biologists began to have an inkling as to how some of this machinery worked.

In the human being there is a large gland called the pancreas. It manufactures a digestive juice which enters the small intestine and mixes with food emerging from the stomach. The interesting thing is that the pancreas doesn't bother wasting its juice when the small intestine is empty. Nothing happens until food enters the small intestine and then, instantly, the pancreatic juice starts flowing.

Something automatic must be involved and in 1902, two English biologists, William Maddock Bayliss and Ernest Henry Starling, discovered what it was.

The food in the stomach is mixed with a strongly acid juice. When the food emerges from the stomach and enters the small intestine, the touch of its acidity has a chemical effect on the intestinal lining and causes it to produce a substance which Bayliss and Starling called "secretin."

Secretin is discharged into the bloodstream and is carried to all the body. When it reached the pancreas, it brings about a chemical effect that causes the pancreas to begin to manufacture and discharge its juice.

Secretin is a substance which rouses the pancreas to activity. In 1905, Bayliss suggested that secretin, and all other substances like it, be called "hormones," from a Greek word meaning "to arouse."

The process of molting seems to be an automatic process controlled by a hormone. As the larva grows, there is growing pressure from the cuticle. When the pressure reaches a certain point, a hormone is triggered. It pours into the larva's bloodstream and when it reaches the cuticle that cuticle is made to split.

The hormone that does this has been given the name "ecdysone," from a Greek word meaning "to molt."

But molting doesn't go on forever. After a certain number of molts, there is a sudden change. Instead of continuing to grow in order to prepare the way for still another molt, the larva begins to undergo metamorphosis instead.

Can this be because a second hormone is involved? Is there a second hormone that suddenly appears after a certain number of molts and brings about the metamorphosis?

Not quite. In 1936, an English biologist, Vincent Brian Wigglesworth, was working with a certain disease-spreading, blook-sucking bug called *Rhodnius*. In the course of his experiments, he thought it would be useful to see what would happen if he cut off the head of the larva of these bugs.

Naturally, if you cut off the head of a mammal or a bird, the creature would die and that would be all. An insect, however, is far less dependent on its head, and life could continue in some ways.

But different parts of the body produce different hormones and some can be produced in the head. By cutting off the head of a larva, Wigglesworth could tell what hormones the insect head might be producing. After all, the headless larva would grow differently than one with a head would and the differences might be at least partly due to the missing head-hormones.

Wigglesworth did indeed notice a change. As soon as he had cut off the head, the larva went into a molt and emerged as an adult. (*Rhodnius* was not one of the bugs that went through a pupa stage.)

It did this even when it was nowhere near ready for such a change. It hadn't molted enough times; it was far too small. Yet it did change and a miniature adult would appear.

But if metamorphosis was caused by the production of a hormone, how could cutting off the head produce it? Cutting off the head should cause the loss of a hormone, not its production.

Wigglesworth argued that the head produced a hormone that *prevented* metamorphosis. As long as it was produced, ecdysone, the molting hormone, did its work; the larva molted and grew, molted and grew. At a certain point, though, in the course of the life of the normal insect, something happened which cut off the supply of this head hormone. Without that hormone, ecdysone couldn't work even though it was present, and metamorphosis began.

If the head were cut off, the supply of the hormone was destroyed at once and metamorphosis began even though the insect body wasn't really ready for it.

Wigglesworth called this hormone from the insect head "juvenile hormone" because it kept the insect in its juvenile, or youthful, form. He also located tiny glands, barely visible without a microscope, behind the brain of the larva and these, Wigglesworth was certain, produced the hormone.

What Wigglesworth found to be true of *Rhodnius* was true of other insects, too; of the silkworm caterpillar, for instance. It seems that all insects that undergo metamorphosis do so because the supply of juvenile hormone stops at a certain time.

Wigglesworth's suggestion about the glands in the head was quickly shown to be correct. In 1938, a French biologist, Jean Bounhiel, worked out a delicate technique for removing the tiny hormone-producing glands from a small silkworm caterpillar and placing them in a large one.

The large silkworm caterpillar was about ready to enter its pupal stage, which meant that its glands had stopped producing juvenile hormone. The glands from the small caterpillar, however, were still capable of producing the hormone. When the glands from the small caterpillar were grafted into the large one, the large caterpillar suddenly found itself with a new supply of juvenile hormone. Instead of entering the pupal stage, it continued to molt one or two extra times.

Naturally, it continued to grow, too, and when it finally did switch to the pupa, it was a considerably larger-than-normal one, and out of it emerged a considerably larger-than-normal adult moth.

At this point, Carroll Williams of Harvard University stepped onto the scene. He transferred hormone-producing glands, not to another larva, but to the pupa of a silkworm. The pupa was well along in metamorphosis. It wasn't supposed to be exposed to any juvenile hormone at all; it was past that stage. But what if juvenile hormone were forced upon it?

Williams had his answer at once. The presence of juvenile hormone seemed to stop the metamorphosis, or at least slow it down. When the adult moth finally appeared it was incomplete. Some of it had not changed over.

Williams found that the more gland material he inserted into the pupa, the more incomplete the metamorphosis. He could use the amount of incompleteness of metamorphosis to judge how much juvenile hormone were present in the glands at different stages in the life of the larva.

He could also determine if there were juvenile hormone anywhere else in an insect body, and here he stumbled over something that was a complete surprise.

In 1956, Williams found that an insect called the "Cecropia moth" produced a large quantity of juvenile hormone just before entering the adult stage, after having passed through the pupa stage entirely without it. Why they do this nobody knows.

This juvenile hormone is stored in the abdomen of the moth for some reason. Only the male moth does it, not the female. Only one other kind of moth, as far as is known, stores juvenile hormone in this fashion. All other insects do not.

Even if biologists don't know the reason for any of this, it still turned out to be a useful fact. The tiny glands that produce juvenile hormone in larvas contain so little that it is just about impossible to extract a useful amount. The reserve supply in the abdomen of the male Cecropia moth is so large, on the other hand, that the hormone can be produced in visible quantities.

Williams produced an extract from the abdomens of many such moths; a few drops of golden oil that contained huge quantities of juvenile hormone. Now he had plenty of material with which he could experiment further.

One Cecropia abdomen supplied enough hormone to block completely the metamorphosis of ten pupas of almost any kind of moth or butterfly. The extract did not even have to be injected into the pupa. If some were just applied to the skin of the pupa, enough hormone leaked into the inner tissues to upset the metamorphosis.

The metamorphosis could be so badly upset, if enough juvenile hormone were used, that the pupa could not develop at all. It simply died.

The thought at once occurred to Williams that here might be a potential insecticide that would have great advantages over every other kind known. After all, it turned the insect's own chemistry against itself.

An insect couldn't grow resistant to juvenile hormone, as it could to any other sort of insecticide. It had to respond to its own hormones. If it didn't, it would die.

In other words, an insect had to respond to juvenile hormone at the right time or it would die. And if it did respond at the right time, then it would also respond at the wrong time and *still* die. Either way, the insect was dead.

Even more important, the juvenile hormone would be no

danger to forms of life other than insects. It affected only insects and has no effect whatever (as far as has been found so far) on any form of life other than insects.

Of course, it is one thing to kill a few pupas in a laboratory and quite another to kill vast quantities out in the fields. Thousands of tons of insecticides are needed for the work that must be done and it would be impossible to get thousands of tons out of Cecropia moths.

If only the chemical structure of the juvenile hormone were known. It would then be possible to manufacture it from other chemicals; or else manufacture something that was close enough to do the job. Unfortunately, the structure was not known.

Williams and a colleague, John Law, sat in their Harvard Laboratories one summer day in 1962, wondering if they could reason out what the structure *might* be. A lab assistant, listening to them, suggested a particular type of compound as a joke.

John Law thought he would go along with the gag. It wouldn't be too difficult to make the compound, or something with a name very like the lab assistant's joke. With scarcely any trouble at all, he produced an oily solution of a mixture of substances which he intended to show the young assistant and say, "Well, here is the compound you joked about."

Still as long as he had it, he tried it first on insect pupas.

To John Law's everlasting surprise, it worked! It worked unbelievably well. It was over a thousand times as powerful as the extract from Cecropia abdomens. An ounce of Law's solution would kill all the insects over an area of two and one-half acres—at least all the insects that were metamorphosing.

This substance is "synthetic juvenile hormone." It contains at least four different chemicals, and none of them seems to have a structure like that of the natural hormone.

Synthetic juvenile hormone works on all insects tested, including the mosquito that spreads yellow fever and the louse that spreads typhus. Yet it doesn't affect any creature other than insects. It would be no danger to birds, fish, mammals, or man.

Still, killing *all* insects is a little too much. That would upset the balance of nature.

We want to kill only certain insects, only one species out of a thousand. This could be done perhaps with the natural juvenile hormone. Each different group of species of insects manufactures its own kind of juvenile hormone which works for itself but not for others. Perhaps then, you can use a particular juvenile hormone and get just the insect you're after and no other kind.

For instance, a biologist in Prague, Czechoslovakia, named Karel Sláma, was trying to make natural juvenile hormone work on a harmless insect called the "red linden bug." He used the technique developed by Carroll Williams, but the extract from Cecropia moths didn't affect the red linden bugs. It might kill moths and butterflies but it had no effect at all on the red linden bugs. The red linden bugs must have a juvenile hormone so different from those of moths and butterflies that the effects didn't cross.

Williams heard of these experiments and was most curious. In the summer of 1965, Williams asked Sláma to bring his red linden bugs to Harvard and to come with them. Sláma came, and together the two men began to raise the bugs. In Prague, Sláma had grown them by the tens of thousands and their way of growing was always the same. The larvas went through exactly five molts and then moved into the adult stage. (The red linden bug does not go through a pupa stage.)

Yet at Harvard this did not happen. Bug after bug went through the fifth molt. Then, instead of changing into an adult, they stayed larvas and tried to molt a sixth time. Usually, they didn't make it, but died. In the few cases where a bug survived the sixth molt, they died when they attempted a seventh molt. About 1,500 insects died in the Harvard laboratories, where none had died in Prague.

Why? It was as though the bugs had received a dose of juvenile hormone and couldn't stop being larvas—but no juvenile hormone had been given them.

Williams and Sláma tried to think of all possible differences between the work at Harvard and the work in Prague. In Harvard, the red linden bugs were surrounded by all sorts of other insects which were involved in juvenile hormone experiments. Perhaps some of the hormone got across somehow. The other insects were therefore removed but the red linden bugs still died.

Could the glassware have been contaminated during cleaning? Maybe. So Williams ordered new glassware that had never been used. The bugs still died.

Could there be something wrong with the city water? Williams got spring water, but the bugs still died.

Altogether fourteen different possibilities were thought of and thirteen were cancelled out. One thing remained, and one only—

Strips of paper were placed into the jars in which the red linden bugs were grown. They were slanted against the sides, as a kind of path for the bugs to scurry along. (That seemed to keep them more active and in better health.) Of course, the paper used at Harvard was not the same as the paper used in Prague. Williams was, in fact, using strips of ordinary paper towels produced by a local manufacturer.

Williams proceeded to check that. He used strips of chemically pure filter paper instead. At once, the bugs stopped dying.

There was something in the paper towels that acted like juvenile hormone and upset the chemical machinery of the larvas. It kept them molting after they should have stopped doing so and that killed them. Williams called the mysterious substance that did this the "paper factor." Later, it received the more chemical sounding name of "juvabione."

Williams and Sláma went on to try all kinds of paper. They found that almost any American newspaper and magazine contained the factor. Red linden bug larvas that crawled over them never made it to the adult stage. On the other hand, paper from Great Britain, the European continent, or Japan, did not have it and the bugs lived well on such paper. (That's why they lived in Prague.)

Could it be that American manufacturers put something in paper that other manufacturers did not? A check with the manufacturers showed they didn't. Well, then, what about the trees from which the paper was made.

They began to test extracts from the trees and found one called the "balsam fir" which was much used for American paper but which did not grow in Europe. It was particularly rich in paper factor, and this paper factor could be obtained from the tree in large quantities.

Here is an interesting point. The paper factor works on only one group of insect species, the one to which the red linden bug happens to belong. If Sláma had brought with him some insect from another group of species, the paper factor might have gone undiscovered.

The paper factor is an example of an insecticide that will kill only one small group of insects and won't touch anything else. Not only are fish, birds, and mammals safe, but so are all insects outside that one group of species.

To be sure, the red linden bug is harmless and there is no purpose in killing it, but the red cotton bug, which eats up half of India's cotton crop, is closely related to it. The red cotton bug can also be hit by the paper factor and experiments are underway to see how well it will work in India's cotton fields.

Paper factor catches bugs at the time of their metamorphosis. This is better than nothing but it still isn't quite as good as it might be. By the time the metamorphosis is reached, the insect has spent a lot of time as a larva—eating, eating, eating.

Then any insects that happen to survive the paper factor for some reason can lay a great many eggs. They will develop into larvas that will eat and eat and eat and will only be caught at the metamorphosis.

It would be better if insects were caught at the beginning of the larval stage rather than at the end.

And they can be! It turns out that the eggs, like the period of metamorphosis, must be free of juvenile hormone. In 1966, Sláma placed eggs of the red linden bug on paper containing the factor and—if the eggs were fresh enough and weren't already on the point of hatching—they didn't hatch.

Then he tried it on adult females that were ready to lay eggs but hadn't laid them yet. He placed a drop of the factor on the adult's body and found that it worked its way inside and, apparently, even into the eggs. At least such a female laid eggs that didn't hatch.

The paper factor was more valuable than ever now, for it could be used to catch the insects at the very beginning of their life.

But why should the balsam fir possess a compound that acts like juvenile hormone? The answer seems clear. Insects eat plants and plants must have developed methods of self-protection over the millions of years of evolution.

A good method of self-protection is for the plants to develop substances that taste bad to insects or that kill them. Plants which happen to develop such substances live and flourish better than those that don't.

Naturally, a plant would develop a substance that would affect the particular insects that are dangerous to it. It seemed that if biologists were to make extracts from a large variety of plants, they might find a variety of substances that would kill this type of insect or that. In the end, they would have, perhaps, a whole collection of insecticides to use on particular insect pests. We would be able to attack only the insects we want to attack and leave the rest of nature alone. By 1968, indeed, some fifteen such plant self-defense chemicals were located.

Then, too, in 1967, Williams took another step in this direction, while with an expedition exploring the interior of the South American country Brazil. There the large river Rio Negro flows into the Amazon. The name means "Black River" because its waters are so dark.

Williams noticed there were surprisingly few insects about the banks of the river and wondered if the trees might not contain considerable paper factor of different kinds. Then he wondered if the darkness of the river water might not come from its soaking substances out of the trees that lined its bank. If so, the river water might contain all kinds of paper factors.

Tests have shown that the Rio Negro does have insecticide properties. Perhaps many different paper factors will be extracted from it in endless supply. Perhaps other rivers may be found to be as useful.

In 1968, Sláma synthesized a hormonelike compound which was the most powerful yet. An insect treated with such a hormone would pass a bit of it on to any other insect with which it mated. One treated insect could sterilize hundreds of others.

So things look quite hopeful. Between the supplies found in nature and between the chemicals that can be formed in the laboratory, we may get our insect enemies at last.

This will mean that man's supply of food and fiber will increase. It will mean that a number of diseases will no longer threaten him, and he will be able to work harder to produce goods.

In that case, we may well be able to feed, clothe, and take care of all the billions who will swell Earth's population in the next forty years or so. . . . And by that time we may have learned to control our own numbers and we will then be safe.

2—IN THE BEGINNING

The first chapter dealt with a scientific search that had a very practical goal—ways of killing dangerous insects. When you solve the problem, there is no mistake about it; the insects die.

But there are also problems that are much more difficult to tackle; problems that are so complicated it is even hard to tell whether we are on the road to solving them, or just in a blind alley. Yet they are problems so important that man's curiosity forces him to tackle them anyway.

Consider the question: What is life?

There is no plain answer yet and some scientists wonder if there ever can be. Even the simplest form of life is composed of very complex substances that are involved in so many numerous complicated chemical changes that it is almost hopeless to try to follow them. What parts of those changes make up the real basis of life? Do any of them?

The problem is so enormous that it is like a continent that must be explored at different points. One group of explorers follows a huge river inland; another group may follow jungle trails elsewhere; while a third sets up a camel caravan into the desert.

In the same way, some biologists analyze the behavior of

living animals under various conditions; others study the structure of portions of tissue under microscopes while still others separate certain chemicals from tissue and work with them. All such work contributes in its own way to increasing knowledge concerning life and living things.

Enormous advances have indeed been made. The two greatest biological discoveries of the nineteenth century were 1) that all living creatures are constructed of cells, and 2) that life has slowly developed from simple creatures to more complex ones.

The first discovery is referred to as the "cell theory," the second as the "theory of evolution."

Both theories made the problem of life seem a little simpler. Cells are tiny droplets of living substance marked off from the rest of the world by a thin membrane. They are surprisingly alike no matter what creature they are found in. A liver cell from a fish and one from a dog are much more similar than the whole fish and dog are.

Perhaps if one could work out all the details of what makes individual cells alive, it would not be so difficult to go on and get an understanding about whole creatures.

Then, too, consider that there was a gradual development of complex organisms from simpler ones. In that case, it might well be that all creatures that exist today developed from the same very simple one that existed long ages ago. There would then be only one form of life, existing in many different varieties. If you understood what made a housefly alive, or even a germ, you ought then understand what makes a man alive.

But these nineteenth century theories also raised a new problem. The more people investigated cells and evolution, the more clear it became that all living creatures came from other living creatures; all cells came from other cells. New life, in other words, is only formed from old life. You, for example, are born of your parents.

Yet there must have been a time in the early history of the

Earth when there was no life upon it. How, then, did life come to be? This is a crucial question, for if scientists knew how the first life was formed on a world that had no life on it, they might find they had taken a big step forward in understanding what life is.

Some nineteenth century scientists were aware of this question and understood its importance. Charles Darwin, the English biologist who first presented the theory of evolution to the world in its modern form, speculated on the subject. In a letter written to a friend in 1871, he wondered if the kind of complex chemicals that make up living creatures might not have been formed somewhere in a "warm little pond" where all the ingredients might be present.

If such complex compounds were formed nowadays, tiny living creatures existing in that pond would eat them up at once. In a world where there was no life, however, such compounds would remain and accumulate. In the end, they might perhaps come together in the proper way to form a very simple kind of life.

But how can one ever find out? No one can go back billions of years into the past to look at the Earth as it was before life was on it. Can one even be sure what conditions were like on such an Earth, what chemicals existed, how they would act?

So fascinating was the question of life's origin, however, that even if there was no real information, some scientists were willing to guess.

The twentieth century opened with a very dramatic guess that won lots of attention. The person making the guess was a well-known Swedish chemist, Svante August Arrhenius. In 1908, he published a book, *Worlds in the Making,* in which he considered some new discoveries that had recently been made.

It had just been shown that light actually exerted a push

against anything it shone upon. This push was very small, but if the light were strong and an object were tiny, the light-push would be stronger than gravity and would drive the object away from the Sun.

The size of particles that could most easily be pushed by sunlight was just about the size of small cells. Suppose cells were blown, by air currents, into the thin atmosphere high above the Earth's surface. Could they then be caught by the push of sunlight and driven away from the Earth altogether? Could they then go wandering through space?

That might be so but wouldn't the cells then die after having been exposed to the vacuum of outer space?

Not necessarily. It had also been discovered that certain bacterial cells could go into a kind of suspended animation. If there was a shortage of food or water, they could form a thick wall about themselves. Within the wall, the bit of life contained in the cell could wait for years, if necessary, without food or water from the outside. They could withstand freezing cold or boiling heat. Then, when conditions had improved, the wall would break away and the bacterial cell could start to live actively once more.

Such walled cells in suspended animation are called "spores." Arrhenius argued that such spores, driven by the push of light, could wander through space for many years, perhaps for millions of years, without dying.

Eventually, such spores might strike some object. It might be some tiny asteroid or some other cold world without air or water. The spore would have to remain a spore forever, until even its patient spark of life winked out. Or it might strike a world so hot as to cause it to scorch to death.

But what if the spore struck a world with a warm, pleasant atmosphere and with oceans of water? Then it would unfold and begin to live actively. It would divide and redivide and form many cells like itself. Over long periods of time, these cells would grow more complicated. They would evolve and form many-celled creatures. In the end, the whole planet would become a home for millions of species of life.

Is that how life originated on Earth itself, perhaps? Once long ago; billions of years ago; did a spore from a far distant planet make its way into Earth's atmosphere? Did it fall into Earth's ocean and begin to grow? Is all the life on Earth, including you and I, the descendant of that little spore that found its way here?

It was a very attractive theory and many people were pleased with it, but alas, there were two things wrong with it.

In the first place, it wouldn't work. It was true that bacterial spores would survive many of the conditions of outer space, but not all. After Arrhenius' book had been published, astronomers began to learn more about what it was like in outer space. They learned more about the sun's radiation for instance.

The sun gives out not visible light alone, but all kinds of similar radiation that might be less energetic or more energetic than light itself.

It radiates infrared waves and radio waves, which are less energetic than ordinary light. It also radiates ultraviolet waves and x rays, which are more energetic than ordinary light. The more energetic radiation is dangerous to life.

Much of the energetic radiation is absorbed by Earth's atmosphere. None of the x rays and very little ultraviolet manage to make their way down to Earth's surface, under a blanket of air miles and miles thick. Even so, if we stand on the beach on a sunny summer day, enough ultraviolet light reaches us to penetrate the outer layers of the skin and to give us sunburn (if we are fair-skinned).

In outer space, the ultraviolet light and x rays are present in full force. They easily penetrate a spore wall and kill the spark of life inside.

If spores were drifting toward our solar system from other

stars, they might strike the outermost planets without harm, but on Pluto or on Neptune they would find conditions too cold for development. As they drifted inward toward Earth, they would be coming into regions where sunlight was stronger and stronger. Long before they could actually reach our planet, the energetic radiation in sunlight would have killed them.

It would seem then that spores, giving rise to the kind of life we now have on Earth, couldn't possibly have reached Earth alive.

Then, too, another flaw in Arrhenius' theory is that it doesn't really answer the question of how life began. It just pushes the whole problem back in time. It says that life didn't begin on Earth but on some other planet far away and long ago and that it reached our world from that other planet. In that case, how did life start on that other planet? Did it reach that other planet from still another planet?

We can go back and back that way but we must admit that originally life must have started on *some* planet from non-living materials. Now that is the question. How did life do that? And if life started *somewhere* from non-living materials, it might just as well have done so on Earth.

So don't let's worry about the possibility of life starting elsewhere and reaching Earth. Let us concentrate on asking how life might have started on earth itself from non-living materials.

Naturally, we ought to try to make the problem as simple as possible. We wouldn't expect non-living substances to come together and suddenly form a man, or even a mouse, or even a mosquito. It would seem reasonable that before any creature even as complicated as a mosquito was formed, single cells would have come into existence; little bits of life too small to be seen except under a microscope.

Creatures exist, even today, that are made up of just one

cell. The amoeba is such a creature. Thousands of different species of one-celled plants and animals exist everywhere. There are also the bacteria, which are composed of single cells even smaller than those of the one-celled plants and animals.

But these cells are complicated, too; very complicated. They are surrounded by membranes made up of many thousands of complex molecules arranged in very intricate fashion. Inside that membrane are numerous small particles that have a delicately organized structure.

It seems hopeless to expect the chemicals in a non-living world to come together and suddenly form even as much as a modern bacterial cell. We must get down to things that are even simpler.

Every cell contains chemicals that don't seem to exist in the non-living world. When such chemicals are found among non-living surroundings, we can be sure that those surroundings were once alive, or that the substances were originally taken from living cells.

This seems to be so clear that early in the nineteenth century chemists began to speak of two kinds of substances. Chemicals that were associated with living creatures, or organisms, were called "organic." Those that were not were "inorganic."

Thus, wood and sugar are two very common organic substances. They are certainly not alive in themselves. You may be sitting in a wooden chair, and you can be sure that it is no more alive than if it were made of stone. However, that wood, as you know very well, was once part of a living tree.

Again, the sugar you put on your morning cereal is certainly not alive. Still, it was once part of a living sugar cane or sugar beet plant.

Salt and water, on the other hand, are inorganic substances. They are found in all living organisms, to be sure; your own tears, for instance, are nothing but a solution of salt in water. However, they are not found *only* in organisms and did not originate *only* in organisms. There is a whole ocean of salt water that we feel pretty sure existed in some form or other before life appeared on this planet.

(Beginning in the middle of the nineteenth century, chemists began to form new compounds that were not to be found in nature. They were very similar in many ways to organic compounds, though they were never found in living organisms or anywhere else outside the chemists' test tubes. These "synthetic" compounds were, nevertheless, lumped together with the organic group because of the similarity in properties.)

It would seem then we could simplify our problem. Instead of asking how life began out of non-living substances, we could begin by asking how organic substances came to be formed out of inorganic substances in the absence of life.

To answer that question, we ought to know in what way organic substances differ from inorganic ones.

Both organic and inorganic substances are made up of "molecules"; that is, of groups of atoms that cling together for long periods of time. Organic molecules are generally larger and more complicated than inorganic ones. Most inorganic molecules are composed of a couple of dozen atoms at most; sometimes only two or three atoms. Organic molecules, however, usually contain well over a dozen atoms and may, indeed, be made up of hundreds, thousands, or even millions of atoms.

When we ask how organic compounds may be formed from inorganic compounds, then, we are really asking how large and complicated molecules might be formed from small and simple ones.

Chemists know that to force small and simple molecules to join together to form large and complicated ones, energy must be added. This is no problem, really, for a very common source of a great deal of energy is sunlight, and in the early lifeless Earth, sunlight was certainly blazing down upon the ocean. We will come back to that later.

It is also true that the different kinds of atoms within molecules cannot change their nature under ordinary circumstances. The large organic molecules in living matter must be formed from small and simple molecules that contain the same kinds of atoms.

We must ask ourselves what kinds of atoms organic molecules contain.

There are over a hundred different kinds of atoms known today (each kind making up a separate "element"). Over eighty are found in reasonable quantities in the inorganic substances making up the Earth's crust. Only half a dozen of these elements, however, make up the bulk of the atoms in organic molecules.

The six types of atoms occurring most frequently in organic molecules are carbon, hydrogen, oxygen, nitrogen, phosphorus, and sulfur. We can let each one be represented by its initial letter: C, H, O, N, P, and S. The initial letters could also stand for a single atom of each element. C could be a carbon atom, H a hydrogen atom, and so on.

Of these elements, carbon is, in a way, the crucial one. Carbon atoms can combine with each other to form long chains, which can branch in complicated ways. They can also form single rings or groups of rings; or, for that matter, rings with chains attached. To the carbon atoms arranged in any of these ways, other atoms can be attached in different manners.

These complicated chains and rings of carbon atoms are found only in organic compounds, never in inorganic compounds. It is this which makes organic molecules larger and more complicated than inorganic ones.

Carbon atoms can be hooked together in so many ways, and can attach other atoms to themselves in so many ways that there is almost no end to the different variations. And each different variation is a different substance with different properties.

Hundreds of thousands of different organic compounds are known today. Every year many more organic compounds are discovered and there is no danger of ever running out of new ones. Uncounted trillions upon trillions of such compounds can exist.

This seems to make the problem of the origin of life more difficult again. If we are trying to find out how organic substances are formed from inorganic ones, and if there are uncounted trillions upon trillions of organic substances possible, how can we decide *which* organic substance ought to be formed and which were formed in the past.

Suppose, though, we can narrow down the choice. Not all organic compounds are equally vital to life. Some of them seem to be more central to the basic properties of life than others are.

All cells without exception, whether plant, animal, or bacterial, seem to be built about two kinds of substances that are more important than any others. These are "proteins" and "nucleic acids."

Even viruses can be included here. They are tiny objects, far smaller than even the smallest cells, yet they seem to be alive since they can invade cells and multiply there. They, too, contain proteins and nucleic acids. Some viruses, in fact, contain practically nothing else *but* proteins and nucleic acids.

Now we have narrowed the problem. We must not ask how organic compounds were built up out of inorganic ones, but how proteins and nucleic acids were built up out of them.

That still leaves matters complicated enough. Both proteins and nucleic acids are made up of very large molecules, often containing millions of atoms. It is too much to expect that small inorganic molecules would come together suddenly to form a complete molecule of protein or nucleic acid.

Let's look more closely at such giant molecules. Both proteins and nucleic acids are composed of simpler structures strung together like beads on a necklace. Both protein and nucleic acid molecules can be treated chemically in such a way that the string breaks and the individual "building blocks" separate. They can then be studied separately.

In the case of the protein molecule, the building blocks are called "amino acids." The molecule of each amino acid is built around a chain of three atoms, two of which are carbon and one nitrogen. We can write this chain as -C-C-N-.

There would be different atoms attached to each of these. The atoms attached to the carbon and nitrogen atoms at the end are always the same in all the amino acids obtained from proteins (with a minor exception we needn't worry about). The carbon atom in the middle, however, can have any of a number of different atom-groupings attached to it. If we call this atom-grouping R, then the amino acid would look like this: -C-C-N-
$$\begin{array}{c} | \\ R \end{array}$$

Each different structure for R results in a slightly different amino acid. Altogether there are nineteen different amino acids that are found in almost every protein molecule. The simplest R consists of just a hydrogen atom. The rest all contain different numbers of carbon and hydrogen atoms, while some contain one or two oxygen atoms in addition, or one or two nitrogen atoms, or even one or two sulfur atoms. Individual amino acids are made up of from eleven to twenty-six atoms.

Although there are only nineteen different amino acids in most proteins, they can be put together in many different ways, each way making up a slightly different molecule. Even a middle-sized protein molecule is made up of several hundred of these amino acids and the number of different combinations is enormous.

Imagine yourself to be given several hundred beads of nineteen different colors and that you set to work to string them. You could make necklaces of many trillions of different color combinations. In the same way, you could imagine protein molecules of many trillions of different amino acid combinations.

In thinking of the origin of life, then, you don't have to worry, just at first, about forming complicated protein molecules. That would come later. To begin with, it would be satisfying to know whether the amino acid building blocks could be formed and, if so, how.

The nucleic acids are both simpler and more complicated than the protein. Nucleic acid molecules are made up of fewer different kinds of building blocks but the individual building block is more complicated.

The huge nucleic acid molecule is made up of long chains of smaller compounds known as "nucleotides," each of which is made up of about three dozen atoms. These include carbon, hydrogen, oxygen, nitrogen, and phosphorus.

An individual nucleotide molecule is made up of three parts. First there is a one-ring or two-ring combination made up of carbon and nitrogen atoms. If there is only one ring, this portion is called a "pyrimidine"; two rings is a "purine."

The second portion is made up of a ring of carbon and oxygen atoms. This comes in two varieties. One is called "ribose"; the other, with one fewer oxygen atom, is "deoxyribose." Both these compounds belong to the class called sugars.

Finally, the third part is a small atom group containing a phosphorus atom. It is the "phosphate group."

We might picture a nucleotide as follows:

$$\frac{\text{purine or}}{\text{pyrimidine}} - \frac{\text{ribose or}}{\text{deoxyribose}} - \frac{\text{phosphate}}{\text{group}}$$

There are two kinds of nucleic acid molecules. One of them is built up of nucleotides that all contain ribose. This is, therefore, "ribosenucleic acid" or RNA. The other is built up of nucleotides that all contain deoxyribose; "deoxyribosenucleic acid" or DNA.

In both cases, individual nucleotides vary in the particular kind of purine or pyrimidine they contain. Both RNA and DNA are made up of chains of four different nucleotides. Even though there are only four different nucleotides, so many of them are present in each enormous nucleic acid molecule that they can be arranged in trillions upon trillions of different ways.

Now that we have decided we want to form amino acids and nucleotides out of inorganic compounds, we must ask out of what inorganic compounds we can expect them to be formed. We must have inorganic compounds, to start with, that contain the right atoms: carbon, hydrogen, oxygen, and the rest.

To begin with, there is the water molecule in the oceans. That is made up of two hydrogen atoms and an oxygen atom and it can therefore be written H_2O. Then there is the carbon dioxide of the air, which dissolves in the ocean water and which is made up of a carbon atom and two oxygen atoms, CO_2. Water and carbon dioxide can supply carbon, hydrogen, and oxygen, three of the necessary elements.

Also dissolved in ocean water are substances that are called nitrates, sulfates, and phosphates. They contain nitrogen atoms, sulfur atoms, and phosphorus atoms respectively. These substances all have certain properties in common with ordinary table salt and can be lumped together as "salts."

What we have to ask ourselves now is this: Is it possible that once long ago, when the world was young, water, carbon dioxide, and salts combined to form amino acids and nucleotides. If so, how was it done?

There are certain difficulties in this thought.

To begin with, in order for water, carbon dioxide, and salts to form amino acids and nucleotides, oxygen atoms must be discarded. There is much more oxygen in water, carbon dioxide, and salts, than there is in amino acids and nucleotides.

But Earth's atmosphere contains a great deal of oxygen. To discard oxygen, when oxygen is already all about, is very difficult. It is like trying to bail the water out of a boat that is resting on the lake bottom.

Secondly, it takes energy to build up amino acids and nucleotides out of simple inorganic molecules and the most likely source is sunlight. Just sunlight isn't enough, however. To get enough energy, you must use the very energetic portion of the sunlight; you must use ultraviolet waves.

But very little of the ultraviolet waves gets down to the surface of the Earth. The air absorbs most of it. When scientists studied the situation more closely it turned out that it was the oxygen in the air that produced the substance that absorbed the ultraviolet.

So oxygen was a double villain. It kept the ultraviolet away from the surface of the Earth and its presence made it very difficult to discard excess oxygen.

To be sure, the plant life that covers the land and fills the sea is carrying through just the sort of thing we are talking about and doing it *right now*. Plants absorb water, carbon dioxide, and salts and use the energy of sunlight to manufacture all sorts of complicated organic compounds out of them. In doing so, they discard oxygen and pour it into the atmosphere.

However, to do this, plants make use of visible light, not ultraviolet waves. Visible light (unlike ultraviolet waves) can penetrate the atmosphere easily, so that it is available for the plants to use. Visible light has considerably less energy than ultraviolet waves but the plants make use of it anyway.

You might wonder if this could not have happened on the early Earth. Suppose the energy of visible light had been used to build up the amino acids and nucleotides.

It doesn't seem likely, though, that it could have happened that way. The reason it happens now is that plants make use of a complicated chemical system that includes a substance known as "chlorophyll." Chlorophyll is an organic compound with a most complicated molecule that is formed only by living organisms.

In thinking of the early Earth, a planet without life on it, we must suppose that chlorophyll was absent. Without chlorophyll, the energy of visible light is not enough to form amino acids and nucleotides. The more energetic ultraviolet waves are necessary and that can't pass through our atmosphere.

We seem to be stuck.

But then, in the 1920s, an English biochemist, John Burdon Sanderson Haldane, suggested that oxygen had not always existed in Earth's atmosphere.

After all, plant life is always using up carbon dioxide and producing oxygen, as it forms organic substances from inorganic substances. Might it not be that all the oxygen that is now in the Earth's atmosphere is the result of plant action? Before there was life, and therefore before there were plants, might not the atmosphere have been made up of nitrogen and carbon dioxide, instead of nitrogen and oxygen, as today?

If that were the case, ultraviolet waves could get right down to the Earth's surface without being much absorbed. And, of course, oxygen could be discarded with much greater ease.

The suggestion turned the whole question in a new direction. It wasn't proper to ask how amino acids and nucleotides might be formed from small compounds that are *now* available under conditions as they exist *now*. Instead we must ask how amino acids and nucleotides might be formed from small compounds that would be available when the Earth was a young and lifeless planet under conditions as they existed *then*.

It became necessary to ask, then, what kind of an atmosphere and ocean the Earth had before life developed upon it.

That depends on what the universe is made up of, generally. In the nineteenth century, ways were worked out whereby the light from the stars could be analyzed to tell us what elements were to be found in those stars (and even in the space between the stars).

Gradually, during the early decades of the twentieth century, astronomers came more and more to the conclusion that by far the most common atoms in the universe were the two simplest: hydrogen and helium. In general, you can say that 90 percent of all the atoms in the universe are hydrogen and 9 percent are helium. All the other elements together make up only 1 percent or less. Of these other elements, the bulk was made up of carbon, nitrogen, oxygen, sulfur, phosphorus, neon, argon, silicon, and iron.

If that is so, then you might expect that when a planet forms out of the dust and gas that fills certain sections of space, it ought to be mostly hydrogen and helium. These are the gases that would make up most of the original atmosphere.

Helium atoms do not combine with any other atoms, but hydrogen atoms do. Because hydrogen atoms are present in such quantities, any type of atom that can combine with hydrogen will do so.

Each carbon atom combines with four hydrogen atoms to form "methane" (CH_4). Each nitrogen atom combines with three hydrogen atoms to form "ammonia" (NH_3). Each sulfur atom combines with two hydrogen atoms to form "hydrogen sulfide" (H_2S). And, of course, oxygen atoms combine with hydrogen to form water.

These hydrogen-containing compounds are all gases, or liquids that can easily be turned into gases, so they would all be found in the primitive atmosphere and ocean.

The silicon and iron atoms, together with those of various other fairly common elements such as sodium, potassium, calcium, and magnesium, don't form gases. They make up the solid core of the planet.

This sort of logic seems reasonable, for a large, cold planet like Jupiter was found, in 1932, to have just this sort of atmosphere. Its atmosphere is chiefly hydrogen and helium, and it contains large quantities of ammonia and methane.

Jupiter is a huge planet, however, with strong gravitation. Smaller planets like Earth, Venus, or Mars, have gravitation that is too weak to hold the very small and very nimble helium atoms or hydrogen molecules. (Each hydrogen molecule is made up of two hydrogen atoms, H_2.)

On Earth, therefore, we would expect the very early atmosphere to contain mostly ammonia, methane, hydrogen sulfide, and water vapor. Most of the water would go to make up the ocean and in that ocean would be dissolved ammonia and hydrogen sulfide. Methane is not very soluble but small quantities would be present in the ocean also.

If we began with such an atmosphere, would it stay like that forever? Perhaps not. Earth is fairly close to the sun and a great deal of ultraviolet waves strike the Earth's atmosphere. These ultraviolet waves are energetic enough to tear apart molecules of water vapor in the upper atmosphere and produce hydrogen and oxygen.

The hydrogen can't be held by Earth's gravity and drifts off into space, leaving the oxygen behind. (Oxygen forms molecules made up of two oxygen atoms each, O_2, and these are heavy enough to be held by Earth's gravity.)

The oxygen does not remain free, however. It combines with the carbon and hydrogen atoms in methane to form carbon dioxide and water. It wouldn't combine with the nitrogen atoms of ammonia, but it would combine with the hydrogen to form water, leaving the nitrogen over to form molecules made up of two atoms each (N_2).

Little by little, as more and more water is broken apart by ultraviolet light, all the ammonia and methane in the atmosphere is converted to nitrogen and carbon dioxide. In fact, the planets Mars and Venus seem to have a nitrogen plus carbon dioxide atmosphere right now.

You might wonder, though, what could happen if all the ammonia and methane were converted to nitrogen and carbon dioxide and if water molecules continued to break up into hydrogen and oxygen. The oxygen would not have anything more to combine with. Perhaps it would gradually accumulate in the air.

This, however, would not happen. As free oxygen accumulates, the energy of sunlight turns some of it into a three-atom combination called "ozone" (O_3). This ozone absorbs the ultraviolet light of the sun and because the ozone layer forms about fifteen miles high in the atmosphere, the ultraviolet light is shielded from the regions of the atmosphere where water vapor exists.

No further water molecules can be broken up and the whole process comes to an end before oxygen can really fill the atmosphere. It is only later on when plants develop and make use of chlorophyll to tap the energy of visible light which *can* get through the ozone layer that the process begins again. After plants come on the scene, the atmosphere fills with oxygen.

So we have three atmospheres for Earth. The first, "Atmosphere I" was chiefly ammonia, methane, and water vapor, with an ocean containing much ammonia in solution. "Atmosphere II" was chiefly nitrogen, carbon dioxide, and water vapor, with an ocean containing much carbon dioxide in solution. Our present atmosphere "Atmosphere III," is chiefly nitrogen, oxygen, and water vapor, with an ocean in which only small quantities of gas are dissolved.

Atmosphere III formed only after life had developed, so life must have originated in the first place in either Atmosphere I or Atmosphere II (or possibly while Atmosphere I was changing into Atmosphere II).

Haldane had speculated that life had originated in Atmosphere II, but a Russian biochemist, Alexander Ivanovich Oparin, thought otherwise.

In 1936, he published a book called *The Origin of Life,* which was translated into English in 1938. Oparin was the first to go into the problem of the origin of life in great detail, and he felt that life must have originated in Atmosphere I.

How was one to decide which was the correct answer? How about experiment? Suppose you were actually to start with a particular mixture of gases that represents an early atmosphere and add energy in the way it might have been added on the early Earth. Will more complicated compounds be formed out of simple ones? And if they are, will they be the kind of compounds that are found in living creatures?

The first scientist who actually tried the experiment was Melvin Calvin at the University of California.

In 1950, he began to work with a portion of Atmosphere II—carbon dioxide and water vapor. The fact that he left out nitrogen meant that he couldn't possibly form nitrogen-containing molecules, like amino acids and nucleotides. However, he was curious to see what he *would* get.

What he needed, to get anything at all, was a source of energy. He might have used ultraviolet waves, the most likely source on the early Earth, but he preferred not to.

Instead, he made use of the energy of certain kinds of atoms that were always exploding. They were "radioactive" atoms. The radioactive elements on Earth are very slowly breaking down so that every year there are very slightly less than the year before. Several billion years ago there must have been twice as much radioactivity in the Earth's crust as there is now. The energy of radioactivity could therefore have been important in forming life.

Since Melvin Calvin was engaged in experimental work that made use of radioactive substances, he had a good supply of them to work with. He bombarded his gas mixture with flying particles released by radioactive atomic explosions.

After a while, he tested the gas mixture and found that in addition to carbon dioxide and water, he had some very simple organic molecules in solution. He had, for instance, a molecule containing one carbon atom, two hydrogen atoms, and one oxygen atom (CH_2O), which was well known to chemists under the name of "formaldehyde." He also had formic acid, which has a second oxygen atom, and has a formula written HCOOH by chemists.

This was just a beginning but it showed a few important things. It showed that molecules could be made more complicated under early Earth conditions. For another the complicated molecules contained less oxygen than the original molecules, so that oxygen was being discarded.

In 1953 came an important turning point, something that was the key discovery in the search for the origin of life. It came in the laboratories of Harold Clayton Urey at the University of Chicago.

Urey was one of those who had tried to reason out the atmosphere of the early Earth, and, like Oparin, he felt it was in Atmosphere I that life might have gotten its start. He suggested to one of his students, Stanley Lloyd Miller, that he set up an experiment in which energy would be added to a sample of Atmosphere I. (At the time Miller was in his early twenties, working for his Ph.D. degree.)

Miller set up a mixture of ammonia, methane, and hydrogen in a large glass vessel. In another glass vessel, he boiled water. The steam that was formed passed up a tube and into the gas mixture. The gas mixture was pushed by the steam through another tube back into the boiling water. The second tube was kept cool so that the steam turned back into water before dripping back into the hot water.

The result was that a mixture of ammonia, methane, hydrogen, and water vapor was kept circulating through the system of vessels and tubes, driven by the boiling water. Miller made very certain that everything he used was completely sterile; that there were no bacteria or other cells in the water or in the gases. (If he formed complicated compounds he wanted to make sure they weren't formed by living cells.)

Next, energy had to be supplied. Urey and Miller reasoned that two likely sources of energy were ultraviolet light from the sun and electric sparks from lightning. (There may have been numerous thunderstorms in Earth's early days.)

Of the two, ultraviolet light is easily absorbed by glass and there was a problem as to how to get enough energy through the glass into the chemicals within. Miller therefore thought that as a first try he would use an electric spark like a small bolt of lightning. Through the gas in one portion of the system he therefore set up a continuing electric spark.

Now it was only necessary to wait.

Something was happening. The water and gases were colorless to begin with, but by the end of one day, the water had turned pink. As the days continued to pass, the color grew darker and darker, till it was a deep red.

After a week, Miller was ready to see what he had formed in his water reservoir. Fortunately, he had at his disposal a new technique for separating and identifying tiny quantities of chemical substances. This is called "paper chromatography" and it had been first developed in 1944 by a group of English chemists.

Like Calvin, Miller found that the simple gas molecules had combined with each other to form more complicated molecules, discarding oxygen atoms.

Again like Calvin, Miller found that formic acid was an important product. He also found, however, that compounds had been formed which were similar to formic acid but were more complicated. These included acetic acid, glycolic acid, and lactic acid, all substances that were intimately associated with life.

Miller had begun with a nitrogen-containing gas, ammonia, which Calvin had lacked. It is not surprising, therefore, that Miller ended up with some molecules that contained nitrogen as well as carbon, hydrogen, and oxygen. He found some hydrogen cyanide, for instance, which is made up of a carbon atom, a hydrogen atom, and a nitrogen atom in its molecule (HCN).

He also found urea, which has molecules made up of two nitrogen atoms, four hydrogen atoms, a carbon atom, and an oxygen atom (NH_2CONH_2).

Most important of all, though, Miller discovered among his products two of the nineteen amino acid building blocks that go to make up the various protein molecules. These were "glycine" and "alanine," the two simplest of all the amino acids, but also the two that appear most frequently in proteins.

With a single experiment, Miller seemed to have accomplished a great deal. In the first place, these compounds had formed quickly and in surprisingly large quantities. One-sixth of the methane with which he had started had gone into the formation of more complex organic compounds.

He had only worked for a week, and with just a small quantity of gas. How must it have been on the early Earth, with its warm ocean, full of ammonia, and with winds of methane blowing over it, all baking under the sun's ultraviolet radiation or being lashed by colossal lightning bolts for a billion years?

Millions of tons of these complex compounds must have been formed, so that the ocean became a kind of "warm soup."

Secondly, the kind of organic molecules formed in Miller's experiment proved particularly interesting. Among the first compounds formed were simple amino acids, the building blocks of proteins. In fact, the path taken by the simple molecules as they grew more complex seemed pointed directly toward life. No molecules were formed that seemed to point in an unfamiliar direction.

Suppose that, as time went on, more and more complicated molecules were built up, always in the direction of compounds now involved with life and not in other directions. Gradually, bigger and bigger molecules would form as building blocks would join together. Finally, something like a real protein molecule and nucleic acid molecule would form and these would eventually associate with each other in a very simple kind of cell.

All this would take a lot of time, to be sure. But then, there was a whole ocean of chemicals to work with, and there was lots of time—a billion years, at least.

Miller's experiment was only a beginning, but it was an extremely hopeful beginning. When its results were announced, a number of biochemists (some of whom were already thinking and working in similar directions) began to experiment in this fashion.

In no time at all, Miller's work was confirmed; that is, other scientists tried the same experiment and got the same results. Indeed, Philip Hauge Abelson, working at the Carnegie Institution of Washington, tried a variety of experiments with different gases in different combinations.

It turned out that as long as he began with molecules that included atoms of carbon, hydrogen, oxygen, and nitrogen somewhere in their structure, he always found amino acids included among the substances formed. And they were always amino acids of the kind that served as protein building blocks.

Nor were electric discharges the only source of energy that would work. In 1959, two German scientists, Wilhelm Groth and H. von Weyssenhoff, tried ultraviolet waves and they also got amino acids.

It could be no accident. There was a great tendency for atoms to click together in such a way as to produce amino acids. Under the conditions that seemed to have prevailed on the early Earth, it appeared impossible not to form amino acids.

By 1968, every single amino acid important to protein structure had been formed in such experiments. The last to be formed were certain important sulfur-containing amino acids, according to a report from Pennsylvania State University and from George Williams University in Montreal.

Perhaps other important compounds also couldn't help but form. Perhaps they would just naturally come together to form the important large molecules of living tissue.

If that is so, life may be no "miracle." It couldn't help forming, any more than you can help dropping downward if you jump off a building. Any planet that is something like the Earth, with a nearby sun and a supply of water and an atmosphere full of hydrogen compounds, would then have to form life. The kinds of creatures that eventually evolved on other worlds would be widely different and might not resemble us any more than an octopus resembles a gorilla. But, the chances are, they would be built up of the same chemical building blocks as we.

More and more, scientists are beginning to think in this way, and they are beginning to speculate that life may be very common in the universe.

Of course, on planets that are quite different from Earth; much bigger and colder, like Jupiter, or much smaller and hotter, like Mercury, our kind of life could not form. On the other hand, other kinds of life, based on other types of chemistry, might be formed. We have no way of telling.

But we are getting ahead of ourselves. Miller's experiments were enough to start speculation of this sort, but it was still important to check matters. A couple of amino acids weren't enough. What about the nucleotides, which served as building blocks for nucleic acids? (Since the 1940s, biochemists have come to believe that nucleic acids are even more important than proteins.)

One could repeat Miller's experiment for longer and longer periods, hoping that more and more complicated molecules would be formed. However, as more and more kinds of compounds were formed, there would be less and less of each separate kind, and it would become more difficult to spot each one.

Possibly, one could start with bigger and bigger quantities of gases in the first place. Even so, the large number of complicated molecules that would be formed would confuse matters.

It occurred to some experimenters to begin not at the beginning of Miller's experiment, but at its end. For instance, one of the most simple products of Miller's experiment was hydrogen cyanide, HCN.

Suppose you assumed that this gas was formed in quantity in Earth's early ocean and then started with it. In that way you would begin partway along the road of development of life and carry it on further.

At the University of Houston, a Spanish-born biochemist, Juan Oro, tried just this in 1961. He found that not only amino acids were formed once he added HCN to the starting mixture, but individual amino acids were hooked together in short chains, in just the way in which they are hooked together in proteins.

Even more interesting was the fact that purines were formed, the double rings of carbon and nitrogen atoms that are found in nucleotides. A particular purine called "adenine" was obtained. This is found not only in nucleic acids but in other important compounds associated with life.

As the 1960s opened, then, imitations of the chemical environment of the early Earth were being made to produce not only the building blocks of the proteins, but the beginnings of the nucleotide building blocks of the nucleic acids.

It was just the beginnings in the latter case. The nucleotides contained not only purines but also the somewhat similar, but simpler, one-ringed compounds, the pyrimidines. Then there were the sugars, ribose and deoxyribose. And, of course, there was the phosphate group.

The experimenters bore on. All the necessary purines and pyrimidines were formed. The sugars proved particularly easy.

Sugar molecules are made up of carbon, hydrogen, and oxygen atoms only. No nitrogen atoms are needed. That reminded one of Calvin's original experiment. Calvin had obtained formaldehyde (CH_2O) from carbon dioxide and water. What if one went a step farther and began with formaldehyde and water.

In 1962, Oro found that if he began with formaldehyde in water and let ultraviolet waves fall upon it, a variety of sugar molecules were formed, and among them were ribose and deoxyribose.

What next?

Purines and pyrimidines were formed. Ribose and deoxyribose were formed. Phosphate groups didn't have to be formed. They existed in solution in the ocean now, and very likely did then, in just the form they existed in inorganic molecules.

One researcher who drove onward was a Ceylon-born biochemist, Cyril Ponnamperuma, at Ames Research Center at Moffett Field, California. He had conducted experiments in which he had, as a beginning, formed various purines with and without hydrogen cyanide. He had formed them through the energy of beams of electrons (very light particles) as well as ultraviolet waves.

In 1963, he, along with Ruth Mariner and Carl Sagan, began a series of experiments in which he exposed a solution of adenine and ribose to ultraviolet waves. They hooked together in just the fashion they were hooked together in nucleotides. If the experimenters began with phosphate also present in the mixture, then the complete nucleotide was formed. Indeed, by 1965, Ponnamperuma was able to announce that he had formed a double nucleotide, a molecule consisting of two nucleotides combined in just the fashion found in nucleic acids.

By the middle 1960s, then, it seemed clear to biochemists that the conditions on the early Earth were capable of leading to the formation of a wide variety of substances associated with life. These would certainly include the amino acids and nucleotides, those building blocks that go to make up the all-important proteins and nucleic acids. Furthermore, these building blocks hook together under early conditions to make up the very chains out of which proteins and nucleic acids are formed.

All the raw materials for life were there on the early Earth, all the necessary chemicals. But life is more than just chemicals. There are all sorts of chemical changes going on in living organisms, and they must be taken into account. Atoms and groups of atoms are shifting here, shifting there, coming apart and reuniting in different ways.

Many of these changes won't take place unless energy is supplied. If we're dealing with the ocean, the energy is supplied by the sun's ultraviolet radiation, or in other ways. But what happens inside the tiny living creatures once they come into existence?

Actually, there are certain chemicals in living creatures which break up easily, releasing energy. Such chemicals make it possible for important chemical changes to take place that would not take place without them. Without such chemicals life as we know it would be impossible no matter how many proteins and nucleic acids built up in the early ocean.

Could it be that some of the energy of sunlight went into the production of these energy-rich compounds? In that case, everything necessary for life might really be supplied.

The best-known of the energy-rich compounds is one called

"adenosine triphosphate," a name that is usually abbreviated as ATP. It resembles a nucleotide to which two additional phosphate groups (making three altogether) have been added.

If, then, adenine, ribose, and phosphate groups are exposed to ultraviolet waves and if they hook together to form a nucleotide containing one phosphate group, perhaps we can go farther. Perhaps longer irradiation or the use of more phosphate to begin with will cause them to hook together to form ATP, with three phosphate groups. Ponnamperuma tried, and it worked. ATP was formed.

In 1967 a type of molecule belonging to a class called "porphyrins" was synthesized from simpler substances by Ponnamperuma. Belonging to this class is the important chlorophyll molecule in green plants.

No one doubts now that all the necessary chemicals of life could have been produced in the oceans of the early Earth by chemical reactions under ultraviolet.

To be sure, the life that was formed at first was probably so simple that we might hesitate to call it life. Perhaps it consisted of a collection of just a few chemicals that could bring about certain changes that would keep the collection from breaking apart. Perhaps it would manage to bring about the formation of another collection like itself.

It may be that life isn't so clear-cut a thing that we can point a finger and say: Right here is something that was dead before and is now alive.

There may be a whole set of more and more complex systems developing over hundreds of millions of years. To begin with, the systems would be so simple that we couldn't admit they were alive. To end with, they would be so complex that we would have to admit they were indeed alive. But where, in between, would be the changeover point?

We couldn't tell. Maybe there is no definite changeover point. Chemical systems might just slowly become more and more "alive" and where they passed the key point, no one could say.

With all the successful production of compounds that followed the work of Calvin and Miller, there still remained the question of how cells were formed. The experimenters who formed compounds recognized that that question would have to be answered somehow.

No one type of compound is living, all by itself. Everything that seems living to us is a mixture of all sorts of substances which are kept close together by a membrane and which react with each other in a very complicated way.

There are viruses, to be sure, which are considered alive and which sometimes consist of a single nucleic acid molecule wrapped in a protein shell. Such viruses, however, don't really get to work in a truly living way till they can get inside some cell. In there, they make use of cell machinery.

Haldane, who had started the modern attack on the problem, wondered how cells might have formed. He pointed out that when oil is added to water, thin films of oil sometimes form bubbles in which tiny droplets of water are enclosed.

Some of the compounds formed by the energy of ultraviolet light are oily and won't mix with water. What if they were to form a little bubble and just happen to enclose a proper mixture of protein, nucleic acid, and other things? Today's cell membrane may be the development of that early oily film.

Oparin, the Russian biochemist, went into further detail. He showed that proteins in solution might sometimes gather together into droplets and form a kind of skin on the outside of those droplets.

The most eager experimenter in this direction, once Miller's work had opened up the problem, was Sidney W. Fox at the University of Miami. It seemed to him that the early Earth must have been a hot planet indeed. Volcanoes may have kept the dry land steaming and brought the ocean nearly to a boil.

Perhaps the energy of heat alone was sufficient to form complex compounds out of simple ones.

To test this, Fox began with a mixture of gases like that in Atmosphere I (the type that Oparin suggested and Miller used) and ran them through a hot tube. Sure enough, a variety of amino acids, at least a dozen, were formed. All the amino acids that were formed happened to be among those making up proteins. No amino acids were formed that were not found in proteins.

Fox went a step farther. In 1958, he took a bit of each of the various amino acids that are found in protein, mixed them together, and heated the mixture. He found that he had driven the amino acids together, higgledy-piggledy, into long chains which resembled the chains in protein molecules. Fox called these chains "proteinoids" (meaning "protein-like"). The likeness was a good one. Stomach juices, which digest ordinary protein, would also digest proteinoids. Bacteria, which would feed and grow on ordinary protein, would also feed and grow on proteinoids.

Most startling of all, when Fox dissolved the proteinoids in hot water and let the solution cool, he found that the proteinoids clumped together in little spheres about the size of small bacteria. Fox called these "microspheres."

These microspheres are not alive, but in some ways they behaved as cells do. They are surrounded by a kind of membrane. Then, by adding certain chemicals to the solution, Fox could make the microspheres swell or shrink, much as ordinary cells do. The microspheres can produce buds, which sometimes seem to grow larger and break off. Microspheres can divide in two or cling together in chains.

Not all scientists accept Fox's arguments, but what if, on the early Earth, more and more complicated substances were built up, turning the ocean into the "warm soup" we spoke of. What if these substances formed microspheres? Might it not be that, little by little, as the substances grew more complicated and the microspheres grew more elaborate, that eventually an almost-living cell would be formed? And after that, a fully living one?

Before life began, then, and before evolutionary changes in cells led to living creatures that were more and more complicated, there must first have been a period of "chemical evolution." In this period, the very simplest gases of the atmosphere and ocean gradually become more and more complicated until life and cells formed.

All these guesses about the origin of life, from Haldane on, are backed up by small experiments in the laboratory and by careful reasoning. Is it possible that we might find traces of what actually happened on the early Earth if we look deep into the Earth's crust.

We find out about ordinary evolution by studying fossils in the crust. These are the remains of ancient creatures, with their bones or shells turned to stone. From these stony remains we can tell what they looked like and how they must have lived.

Fossils have been found deep in layers of rock that must be 600 million years old. Before that we find hardly anything. Perhaps some great catastrophe wiped out the earlier record. Perhaps forms of life existed before then that were too simple to leave clear records.

Actually, in the 1960s discoveries were reported of traces left behind by microscopic one-cell creatures in rocks that are more than two billion years old. Prominent in such research is Elso Sterrenberg Barghoorn of Harvard. It is a good guess that there were simple forms of life on Earth at least as long as three billion years ago.

If we are interested in discovering traces of the period of chemical evolution, then, we must search for still older rocks. In them, we might hope to find chemicals that seem to be on the road to life.

But will chemicals remain unchanged in the Earth for billions of years? Can we actually find such traces if we look for them?

Certainly the important chemicals of life, the proteins and nucleic acids, are too complex to remain unchanged for long after the creature they were in dies and decomposes. In a very short time, it would seem, they must decompose and fall apart.

And yet, it turns out, sometimes they linger on, especially when they are in a particularly well-protected spot.

Abelson, one of the people who experimented with early atmospheres, also worked with fossils. He reasoned that living bones and shell contain protein. Bones may be 50 percent protein. Clam shells have much less, but there is some. Once such bones and shells are buried deep in the Earth's crust, remaining there for millions of years while they turned to stone, it might be that some of the protein trapped between thin layers of mineral might survive. . . . Or at least they might break down to amino acids or short chains of amino acids that might survive.

Painstakingly, Abelson dissolved these ancient relics and analyzed the organic material he extracted. There were amino acids present all right, exactly the same amino acids that are present in proteins of living creatures. He found some even in a fossil fish which might have been 300 million years old.

Apparently, then, organic compounds last longer than one might think and Melvin Calvin began the search for "chemical fossils" in 1961.

In really old rocks, it is unlikely that the organic chemicals would remain entirely untouched. The less hardy portions would be chipped away. What would linger longest would be the chains and rings of carbon atoms, with hydrogen atoms attached. These compounds of carbon and hydrogen only are called "hydrocarbons."

Calvin has isolated hydrocarbons from ancient rocks as

much as three billion years old. The hydrocarbons have molecules of a complicated structure that looked very much as though they could have originated from chemicals found in living plants.

J. William Schopf of Harvard, a student of Barghoorn, has gone even further. He has detected traces of 22 different amino acids in rocks more than three billion years old.

They are probably the remnants of primitive life. It is necessary now to probe farther back and find chemical remnants that precede life and show the route actually taken.

Very likely it will be the route worked out by chemists in their experiments, but possibly it won't be.

We must wait and see. And perhaps increasing knowledge of what went on in the days of Earth's youth will help us understand more about life now.

3—LITTLER AND LITTLER AND . . .

One of the words that fascinates scientists in the 1960s is "quark."

No one has ever seen a quark or come across one in any way. It is far too small to see and no one is even sure it exists. Yet scientists are anxious to build enormous machines costing hundreds of millions of dollars to try to find quarks, *if* they exist.

This is not the first time scientists have looked for objects they weren't sure existed, and were too small to see even if they did exist. They were doing it as early as the very beginning of the nineteenth century.

In 1803, an English chemist, John Dalton, suggested that a great many chemical facts could be explained if one would only suppose that everything was made up of tiny particles, too small to be seen under any microscope. These particles would be so small that there couldn't be anything smaller. Dalton called these particles "atoms" from Greek words meaning "not capable of being divided further." Dalton's suggestion came to be called the "atomic theory."

No one was sure that atoms really existed, to begin with, but they did turn out to be very convenient. Judging by what went on in test tubes, chemists decided that there were a number of different kinds of atoms.

When a particular substance is made up of one kind of atom only, it is an "element." Iron is an element, for instance, and is made up only of iron atoms. Gold is an element; so is the oxygen in the air we breathe.

Atoms can join together into groups and these groups are called "molecules." Oxygen atoms get together in groups of two and these two-atom oxygen groups are called oxygen molecules. The oxygen in the air is made up of oxygen molecules, not of separate oxygen atoms.

Atoms of different elements can come together to form molecules of "compounds." Water is a compound with molecules made up of two hydrogen atoms and one oxygen atom.

Dalton and the nineteenth century chemists who followed him felt that every atom was just a round little ball. There was no reason to think there was anything more to it than that. They imagined that if an atom could be seen under a very powerful microscope, it would turn out to be absolutely smooth and shiny, without a mark.

They were also able to tell that the atom was extremely small. They weren't quite certain exactly how small it was but nowadays we know that it would take about 250 million atoms laid side by side to stretch across a distance of only one inch.

The chief difference between one kind of atom and another kind, in the nineteenth century view, lay in their mass, or weight. Each atom had its own particular mass, or "atomic weight." The hydrogen atom was the lightest of all, and was considered to have an atomic weight of 1. An oxygen atom was about sixteen times as massive as a hydrogen atom, so it had an atomic weight of 16. A mercury atom had an atomic weight of 200, and so on.

As the nineteenth century wore on, the atomic theory was found to explain more and more things. Chemists learned how atoms were arranged inside molecules and how to design new molecules so as to form substances that didn't exist in nature.

By the end of the century, the atomic theory seemed firmly established. There seemed no room for surprises.

And then, in 1896, there came a huge surprise that blew the old picture into smithereens. The chemists of the new twentieth century were forced into a new series of investigations that led them deep into the tiny atom.

What happened in 1896 was that a French physicist, Antoine Henri Becquerel, discovered quite by accident that a certain substance had properties no one had ever dreamed of before.

Becquerel had been interested in x rays, which had only been discovered the year before. He had samples of a substance containing atoms of the heavy metal uranium in its molecules. This substance gave off light of its own after being exposed to sunlight and Becquerel wondered if this light might include x rays.

It didn't, but Becquerel found it gave off mysterious radiations of some kind; radiations that went right through black paper and fogged a photographic film. It eventually turned out that it was the uranium atoms that were doing it. The uranium atoms were exploding and hurling small fragments of themselves in every direction.

Scientists had never expected atoms could explode, but here some of them were doing it. A new word was invented. Uranium was "radioactive."

Other examples of radioactivity were found and physicists began to study the new phenomenon with great interest as the twentieth century opened.

One thing was clear at once. The atom was *not* just a hard, shiny ball that could not be divided into smaller objects. Small as it was, it had a complicated structure and was made up of many objects still smaller than atoms. This had to be, for the uranium atom, in exploding, hurled outward some of these still smaller "subatomic particles."

One of the most skillful of the new experimenters was a New Zealander, Ernest Rutherford. He used the subatomic particles that came flying out of radioactive elements and made them serve as bullets. He aimed them at thin films of metal and found they passed right through the metal without trouble. Atoms weren't hard shiny balls at all. Indeed, they seemed to be mostly empty space.

But then, every once in a while, one of the subatomic bullets would bounce off sharply. It had hit something hard and heavy somewhere in the atom.

By 1911, Rutherford was able to announce that the atom was not entirely empty space. In the very center of the atom was a tiny "atomic nucleus" that contained almost all the mass of the atom. This nucleus was so small that it would take about 100,000 of them, placed side by side, to stretch across the width of a single atom.

Outside the nucleus, filling up the rest of the atom, were a number of very light particles called "electrons." Each different kind of atom had its own particular number of electrons. The hydrogen atom had only a single electron; the oxygen atom had eight; the iron atom had twenty-six; the uranium atom had ninety-two, and so on.

All electrons, no matter what atom they are found in, are alike in every way. All of them, for instance, carry an electric charge. There are two kinds of electric charges—positive and negative. All electrons carry a negative electric charge and the charge is always of exactly the same size. We can say that every electron has a charge of just -1.

The atomic nucleus has an electric charge, too, but a positive one. The charge on the nucleus just balances the charge on the electrons. A hydrogen atom has a single electron with a charge of -1. Therefore, the charge on the hydrogen nucleus is $+1$.

An oxygen atom has eight electrons with a total charge of -8. The oxygen nucleus has a charge of $+8$, therefore.

You can see, then, that the iron nucleus would have to have a charge of +26, the uranium nucleus one of +92, and so on.

Both parts of the atom—the tiny nucleus at the center and the whirling electrons outside—have been involved in unusual discoveries since Rutherford made his announcement in 1911. In this chapter, however, we are going to be concerned only with the nucleus.

Naturally, physicists were interested in knowing whether the atomic nucleus was a single particle. It was so much smaller than the atom that it would seem reasonable to suppose that here at last was something as small as it could be. The atom had proved a surprise, however, and scientists were not going to be too sure of the nucleus either.

Rutherford bombarded atoms with subatomic particles, hoping to discover something about the nucleus if he hit them enough times.

He did. Every once in a while, when one of his subatomic bullets hit a nucleus squarely, that nucleus changed its nature. It became the nucleus of a different variety of atom. Rutherford first discovered this in 1919.

This change of one nucleus into another made it seem as though the nucleus had to be a collection of still smaller particles. Changes would come about because the collection of still smaller particles was broken apart and rearranged.

The smallest nucleus was that of the hydrogen atom. That had a charge of +1 and it did indeed seem to be composed of a single particle. Nothing Rutherford did could break it up (nor have we found a way to do so even today). Rutherford therefore considered it to be composed of a single particle which he called a "proton."

The proton's charge, +1, was exactly the size of the electron's, but it was of the opposite kind. It was a positive electric charge, rather than a negative one.

The big difference between the proton and electron, however, was in mass. The proton is 1,836 times as massive as the electron though to this day physicists don't know why that should be so.

It soon seemed clear that the nuclei of different atoms had different electric charges because they were made up of different numbers of protons. Since an oxygen nucleus had a charge of +8, it must contain eight protons. In the same way, an iron nucleus contained twenty-six protons and a uranium nucleus ninety-two protons.

This is why the nucleus contains just about all the mass of the atom, by the way. The nucleus is made up of protons which are so much heavier than the electrons that circle about outside the nucleus.

But a problem arose at this point that plagued physicists all through the 1920s. The protons could account for the electric charge of the nucleus, but not for all its mass. Because the oxygen nucleus had a charge of +8, it therefore had to contain eight protons, but it also had a mass that was sixteen times as great as a single proton and therefore twice as great as all eight protons put together. Where did the extra mass come from?

The uranium nucleus had a charge of +92 and therefore had to contain ninety-two protons. However, the mass of the uranium nucleus was two and a half times as great as all those ninety-two protons put together. Where did that come from?

Physicists tried to explain this in several ways that proved to be unsatisfactory. A few, however, speculated that there might be particles in the nucleus that were as heavy as protons but that didn't carry an electric charge.

Such uncharged particles, if they existed, would add to the mass of the nuclei without adding to the electric charge. They would solve a great many puzzles concerning the nucleus, but there was one catch.

There seemed no way of detecting such uncharged particles,

if they existed. To see why this is so, let's see how physicists were detecting ordinary charged particles in the 1920s.

Physicists used a number of techniques for the purpose, actually, but the most convenient had been invented in 1911 by a Scottish physicist, Charles Thomson Rees Wilson.

He had begun his career studying weather and he grew interested in how clouds came to form. Clouds consist of very tiny droplets of water (or particles of ice) but these don't form easily in pure air. Instead, each one forms about a tiny piece of dust or grit that happens to be floating about in the upper air. In the absence of such dust, clouds would not form even though the air was filled with water vapor to the very limit it would hold, and more.

It turned out also that a water droplet formed with particular ease, if it formed about a piece of dust that carried an electric charge.

With this in mind, Wilson went about constructing a small chamber into which moist air could be introduced. If the chamber were expanded, the air inside would expand and cool. Cold air cannot hold much water vapor, so as the air cooled the vapor would come out as a tiny fog.

But suppose the moist air introduced into the chamber were completely without dust. Then even if the chamber were expanded and the air cooled, a fog would not form.

Next suppose that a subatomic particle comes smashing through the glass and streaks into the moist air in the chamber. Suppose also that the particle is electrically charged.

Electric charges have an effect on one another. Similar charges (two negatives or two positives) repel each other; push each other away. Opposite charges (a negative and a positive) attract each other.

If a negatively charged particle, like an electron, rushes through the air, it repels other electrons it comes near. It pushes electrons out of the atoms with which it collides. A positively charged particle, like a proton, attracts electrons and pulls them out of the atom. In either case, atoms in the path of electrically charged particles lose electrons.

What is left of the atom then has a positive electrical charge, because the positive charge on the nucleus is now greater than the negative charge on the remaining electrons. Such an electrically charged atom is called an "ion."

Water droplets, which form with particular ease about electrically charged dust particles, also form with particular ease about ions. If a subatomic particle passes through the moist air in the cloud chamber just as that air is cooled, droplets of water will form about the ions that the subatomic particle leaves in its track. The path of the subatomic particle can be photographed and the particle can be detected by the trail it leaves.

Suppose a cloud chamber is placed near a magnet. The magnet causes the moving subatomic particle to curve in its path. It therefore leaves a curved trail of dewdrops.

The curve tells volumes. If the particle carries a positive electric charge, it curves in one direction and if it carries a negative electric charge it curves in the other. The more massive it is, the more gently it curves. The larger its charge, the more sharply it curves.

Physicists took many thousands of photographs of cloud chambers and studied the trails of dewdrops. They grew familiar with the kind of tracks each particular kind of particle left. They learned to tell from those tracks what was happening when a particle struck an atom, or when two particles struck each other.

Yet all of this worked well only for charged particles.

Suppose a particle didn't carry an electric charge. It would have no tendency to pull or push electrons out of an atom. The atoms would remain intact and uncharged. No ions would be formed and no water droplets would appear. In other words, an uncharged particle would pass through a cloud chamber without leaving any sign.

Still, might it not be possible to detect an uncharged particle indirectly? Suppose you faced three men, one of whom was invisible. You would only see two men and if none of them moved you would have no reason to suspect that the third man existed. If, however, the invisible man were suddenly to push one of his neighbors, you would see one of the men stagger. You might then decide that a third man was present but invisible.

Something of the sort happened to physicists in 1930. When a certain metal called beryllium was exposed to a spray of subatomic particles, a radiation was produced by it which could not be detected by cloud chamber.

How did anyone know there was that radiation present then? Well, if paraffin were placed some distance away from the beryllium, protons were knocked out of it. *Something* had to be knocking out those protons.

In 1932, an English physicist, James Chadwick, argued that the radiation from beryllium consisted of uncharged particles. These particles were electrically neutral and they were therefore called "neutrons."

Neutrons were quickly studied, not by cloud chamber, but by the manner in which they knocked atoms about, and much was learned. It was found that the neutron was a massive particle, just a trifle more massive than the proton. Where the proton was 1,836 times as massive as the electron, the neutron was 1,839 times as massive as the electron.

Physicists now found that they had a description of the structure of the nucleus that was better than anything that had gone before. The nucleus consisted of both protons and neutrons. It was the neutrons that accounted for the extra mass of the nucleus.

Thus, the oxygen nucleus had a charge of +8 but a mass of 16. That was because it was made up of 8 protons and 8 neutrons. The uranium nucleus had a charge of +92 and a mass of 238; it was made up of 92 protons and 146 neutrons.

The atomic nucleus, small as it was, did indeed consist of still smaller particles (except in the case of hydrogen). Indeed, the nuclei of the more complicated atoms were made up of a couple of hundred smaller particles.

This does not mean that there weren't some serious questions raised by this proton-neutron theory of nucleus structure.

For instance, protons are all positively charged and positively charged particles repel each other. The closer they are, the more strongly they repel each other. Inside the atomic nucleus, dozens of protons are pushed together so closely they are practically touching. The strength of the repulsion must be enormous and yet the nucleus doesn't fly apart.

Physicists began to wonder if there was a special pull, or force, that held the protons together. This force had to be extremely strong to overcome the "electromagnetic force" that pushed protons apart. Furthermore, the new force had to operate only at very small distances, for when protons were outside nuclei, they repelled each other with no sign of any attraction.

Such a strong attraction that could be felt only within nuclei is called a "nuclear force."

Could such a nuclear force exist? A Japanese physicist, Hideki Yukawa, tackled the problem shortly after the neutron was discovered. He carefully worked out the sort of thing that would account for such an extremely strong and extremely short-range force.

In 1935, he announced that if such a force existed, then it might be built up by the constant exchange of particles by the protons and neutrons in the nucleus. It would be as though the protons and neutrons were tossing particles back and forth and held firmly together as long as they were close enough to toss and catch. As soon as the neutrons and protons were far enough apart so that the particles couldn't reach, then the nuclear force would be no longer effective.

According to Yukawa, the exchange particle should have a mass intermediate between that of the proton and the electron. It was therefore eventually named a "meson" from a Greek work meaning "intermediate."

But did the meson really exist?

The best way of deciding whether it existed and if Yukawa's theory was actually correct was to detect the meson inside the nucleus, while it was being tossed back and forth between protons and neutrons. Unfortunately, that seemed impossible. The exchange took place so quickly and it was so difficult to find out what was going on deep inside the nucleus, that there seemed no hope.

But perhaps the meson could be somehow knocked out of the nucleus and detected in the open. To do that the nucleus would really have to be made to undergo a hard collision.

According to a theory worked out by the German-Swiss physicist, Albert Einstein, in 1905, matter and energy are two different forms of the same thing. Matter is, however, a very concentrated form of energy. It would take the energy produced by burning twenty million gallons of gasoline to make one ounce of matter.

To knock a meson out of the nucleus of an atom would be very much like creating the amount of matter in a meson. To produce that quantity of matter doesn't really take much energy, but that energy has to be concentrated into a single tiny atomic nucleus and doing that turns out to be very difficult.

All through the 1930s and 1940s, physicists devised machines for pushing subatomic particles by electromagnetic forces and making them go faster and faster, piling up more and more energy, until finally, *crash*—they were sent barreling into a nucleus.

Gradually, more and more energy was concentrated into

these speeding particles. Such energy was measured in "electron volts" and by the 1940s particles with energies of ten million electron volts (10 Mev) were produced. This sounds like a great deal, and it is, but it still wasn't enough to form mesons.

Fortunately, physicists weren't entirely stopped. There is a natural radiation ("cosmic rays") striking the Earth all the time. This is made up of subatomic particles of a wide range of energies; some of them are enormously energetic.

They originate somewhere deep in outer space. Even today, physicists are not entirely certain as to the origin of cosmic rays or what makes them possess so much energy. Still, the energy is there to be used.

Cosmic rays aren't the perfect answer. When physicists produce energetic particles, they can aim them at the desired spot. When cosmic rays bombard Earth, they do so without aiming. Physicists must wait for a lucky hit; when a cosmic ray particle with sufficient energy just happens to hit a nucleus in the right way. And then he must hope that someone with a detecting device happens to be at the right place and at the right moment.

For a while, though, it seemed that the lucky break had taken place almost at once. Even while Yukawa was announcing his theory, an American physicist, Carl David Anderson, was high on Pike's Peak in Colorado, studying cosmic rays.

The cosmic ray particles hit atoms in the air and sent other particles smashing out of the atoms and into cloud chambers. When there was finally a chance to study the thousands of photographs that had been taken, tracks were found which curved in such a way as to show that the particle that caused them was heavier than an electron but lighter than the proton. In 1936, then, it was announced that the meson had been discovered.

Unfortunately, it quickly turned out that this meson was a

little too light to be the particle called for by Yukawa's theory. It was wrong in several other ways, too.

Nothing further happened till 1947. In that year, an English physicist, Cecil Frank Powell, was studying cosmic rays far up in the Bolivian Andes. He wasn't using cloud chambers, but special photographic chemicals which darkened when a subatomic particle struck them.

When he studied the tracks in these chemicals, he found that he, too, had a meson, but a heavier one than had earlier been found. Once there was a chance to study the new meson it turned out to have just the properties predicted by Yukawa.

The first meson that had been discovered, the lighter one, was named the "mu-meson." The heavier one that Powell had discovered was the "pi-meson." ("Mu" and "pi" are letters of the Greek alphabet. Scientists often use Greek letters and Greek words in making up scientific names.)

It is becoming more and more common to abbreviate the names of these mesons. The light one is called the "muon" and the heavy one the "pion."

The new mesons are very unstable particles. They don't last long once they are formed. The pion only lasts about twenty-five billionths of a second and then it breaks down into the lighter muon. The only reason the pion can be detected at all is that when it is formed it is usually traveling at enormous speed, many thousands of miles a second. Even in a billionth of a second it has a chance to travel a few inches, leaving a trail as it does so. The change in the kind of trail it leaves toward the end shows that the pion has disappeared and a muon has taken its place.

The muon lasts much longer, a couple of millionths of a second, and then it breaks down, forming an electron. The electron is stable and, if left to itself, will remain unchanged forever.

By the end of the 1940s, then, the atomic nucleus seemed to be in pretty good shape. It contained protons and neutrons and these were held together by pions flashing back and forth. Chemists worked out the number of protons and neutrons in every different kind of atom and all seemed well.

But it did seem that there ought to be two kinds of nuclei— the kind that exists all about us and a sort of mirror image that in the late 1940s, no one had yet seen.

That possibility had first been suggested in 1930 by an English physicist, Paul Adrien Maurice Dirac. He calculated what atomic structure ought to be like according to the latest theories and it seemed to him that every particle ought to have an opposite number. This opposite could be called an "antiparticle."

In addition to an electron, for instance, there ought also to be an "antielectron" that would have a mass just like that of an electron but would be opposite in electric charge. Instead of having a charge of -1, it would have one of $+1$.

In 1932, C. D. Anderson (who was later to discover the muon) was studying cosmic rays. He noticed on one of his photographs a cloud-chamber track which he easily identified as that of an electron. There was only one thing wrong with it; it curved the wrong way. That meant it had a positive charge instead of a negative one.

Anderson had discovered the antielectron. Because of its positive charge, it is usually called a "positron." The existence of the antielectron was strong evidence in favor of Dirac's theory, and as time went on more and more antiparticles were uncovered.

The ordinary muon, for instance, has a negative charge of -1, like the electron, and it is usually called the "negative muon." There is an antimuon, exactly like the muon except that it has a positive charge of $+1$ like the positron. It is the "positive muon."

The ordinary pion is a "positive pion" with a charge of +1. The antipion is the "negative pion" with a charge of −1.

By the close of the 1940s, it seemed quite reasonable to suppose that there were ordinary nuclei made up of protons and neutrons with positive pions shifting back and forth among them; and that there were also "antinuclei" made up of "antiprotons" and "antineutrons" with antipions shifting back and forth.

Physicists didn't really feel they actually had to detect antiprotons and antineutrons to be sure of this but, of course, they would have liked to.

To detect antiprotons is even more difficult than to detect pions. An antiproton is as massive as a proton, which means it is seven times as massive as a pion. To form an antiproton requires a concentration of seven times as much energy as to form a pion.

To form a pion required several hundred million electron volts, but to form an antiproton would require several billion electron volts. (A billion electron volts is abbreviated "Bev.")

To be sure, there are cosmic ray particles that contain several Bev of energy, even several million Bev. The higher the energy level required, however, the smaller the percentage of cosmic ray particles possessing that energy. The chances that one would come along energetic enough to knock antiprotons out of atoms just when a physicist was waiting to take a picture of the results were very small indeed.

However, the machines for producing man-made energetic particles were becoming ever huger and more powerful. By the early 1950s, devices for producing subatomic particles with energies of several Bev were built. One of these was completed at the University of California in March 1954. Because of the energy of the particles it produced, it was called the "Bevatron."

Almost at once, the Bevatron was set to work in the hope that it might produce antiprotons. It was used to speed up protons until they possessed 6 Bev of energy and then those protons were smashed against a piece of copper. The men in charge of this project were an Italian-born physicist, Emilio Segrè, and a young American, Owen Chamberlain.

In the process, mesons were formed; thousands of mesons for every possible antiproton. The mesons, however, were much lighter than antiprotons and moved more quickly. Segrè's group set up detecting devices that would react in just the proper manner to pick up heavy, slow-moving, negatively charged particles. When the detecting devices reacted properly, only something with exactly the properties expected of an antiproton could have turned the trip.

By October 1955, the detection devices had been tripped sixty times. It could be no accident. The antiproton was there and its discovery was announced.

The antiproton was the twin of the proton. The great difference was that the proton had a charge of +1 and the antiproton had a charge of −1.

Once enough antiprotons were produced for study, it was found that occasionally one would pass close by a proton and the opposite charges would cancel. The proton would become a neutron and the antiproton would become an antineutron.

You might wonder how you could tell an antineutron from a neutron since both are uncharged. The answer is that although the neutron and antineutron have no electric charge, they spin rapidly in a way that causes them to behave like tiny magnets. The neutron is like a magnet that points in one direction while the antineutron is like a magnet that points in the opposite direction.

By the mid-1950s, it was clear that antiprotons and antineutrons existed. But could they combine to form an antinucleus?

Physicists were sure they could but the final answer did not come till 1965. In that year, at Brookhaven National

Laboratories in Long Island, New York, protons with energies of 7 Bev were smashed against a beryllium target. Several cases of an antiproton and antineutron in contact were produced and detected.

In the case of ordinary particles, there is an atomic nucleus that consists of one proton and one neutron. This is the nucleus of a rare variety of hydrogen atom that is called "deuterium." The proton-neutron combination is therefore called a "deuteron."

What had been formed at Brookhaven was an "antideuteron." It is the very simplest antinucleus that could be formed of more than one particle, but that is enough. It proved that it could be done. It was proof enough that matter could be built up out of antiparticles just as it could be built of ordinary particles. Matter built up of antiparticles is "antimatter."

When the existence of antiparticles was first proposed, it was natural to wonder why if they could exist, they weren't anywhere around us. When they were detected at last, they were found only in tiny quantities and even those quantities didn't last long.

Consider the positron, or antielectron. All around us, in every atom of all the matter we can see and touch on Earth, are ordinary electrons. Nowhere are there any antielectrons to speak of. Occasionally, cosmic ray particles produce a few or physicists form a few in the laboratory. When they do, those antielectrons disappear quickly.

As an antielectron speeds along, it is bound to come up against one of the trillions of ordinary electrons in its immediate neighborhood. It will do that in perhaps a millionth of a second.

When an electron meets an antielectron, both particles vanish. They are opposites and cancel out. It is like a peg falling into a hole which it fits exactly. Peg and hole both disappear and nothing is left but a flat surface.

In the case of the electron and antielectron, however, not *everything* disappears. Both electron and antielectron have mass, exactly the same amount of the same kind of mass. (We only know of one kind of mass so far.) When the electron and antielectron cancel out, the mass is left over and that turns into energy.

This happens with all other particles and antiparticles. A positive muon will cancel a negative muon; a negative pion will cancel a positive pion; an antiproton will cancel a proton, and so on. In each case both particles disappear and energy takes their place. Naturally, the more massive the particles, the greater the amount of energy that appears.

It is possible to reverse the process, too. When enough energy is concentrated into a small space, particles may be formed out of it. A particle is never formed out of energy by itself, however. If an electron is formed, an antielectron must be formed at the same time. If a proton is formed, an antiproton must be formed at the same time.

When Segrè and Chamberlain set about forming antiprotons, they had to allow for twice as much energy as would be sufficient just for an antiproton. After all, they had to form a proton at the same time.

Since this is so, astronomers are faced with a pretty problem. They have worked up many theories of how the universe came to be, but in all the theories, it would seem that antiparticles ought to be formed along with the particles. There should be just as much antimatter as there is matter.

Where is all this antimatter? It doesn't seem to be around. Perhaps it has combined with matter and turned into energy. In that case, why is there all the ordinary matter about us left over. There should be equal amounts of each, and each set should cancel out the other completely.

Some astronomers suggest that there are two separate universes, one made out of matter (our own) and another made out of antimatter. Other astronomers think there is only one universe but that some parts of it (like the parts near ourselves) are matter, while other parts are antimatter.

What made the matter and antimatter separate into different parts of the universe, or even into different universes, no one can yet say. It may even be possible that for some reason we don't understand, only matter, and no antimatter, was formed to begin with.

The problem of the universe was something for astronomers to worry about, however. Physicists in 1947 were quite satisfied to concentrate on particles and antiparticles and leave the universe alone.

And physicists in that year seemed to have much ground for satisfaction. If they ignored the problem of how the universe began and just concentrated on how it was now, they felt they could explain the whole thing in terms of a little over a dozen particles altogether. Some of these particles they had actually detected. Some they had not, but were sure of anyway.

Of course, not everything was absolutely clear, but what mysteries existed ought to be cleared up, they hoped, without too much trouble.

The particles they knew, or strongly suspected they were soon going to know, fell into three groups, depending on their mass. There were the light particles, the middle-sized particles, and the heavy particles. These were eventually given Greek names from words meaning light, middle-sized, and heavy: "leptons," "mesons," and "baryons."

The leptons, or light particles, include the electron and the antielectron, of course. In order to explain some of the observed facts about electrons, the Austrian physicist Wolfgang Pauli suggested, in 1931, that another kind of particle also existed. This was a very small one, possibly with no mass at all, and certainly with no charge. It was called a "neutrino."

This tiny particle was finally detected in 1956. There was not only a neutrino but also an "antineutrino."

Although the muon was considered a meson, to begin with, it was soon recognized as a kind of heavy electron. All its properties but mass were identical with those of the electron. Along with the muon, a neutrino or antineutrino is also formed as in the case of the electron. In 1962, this muon-neutrino was found to be different from the electron-neutrino.

Two other particles might be mentioned. Light, together with other radiation similar to it (like x rays, for instance) behave in some ways as though they were composed of particles. These particles are called "photons."

There is no antiparticle for a photon; no antiphoton. The photon acts as its own opposite. If you were to fold a sheet of paper down the middle and put the particles on one side and the antiparticles on the other, you would have to put the photon right on the crease.

Then, too, physicists speculate that the reason different objects pull at each other gravitationally is because there are tiny particles called "gravitons" flying between them. Some of the properties of the graviton have been worked out in theory; for instance, it is its own antiparticle. The graviton is so tiny, however, and so hard to pin down, that it has not yet been detected.

This is the total list of leptons so far, then:

1) the graviton
2) the photon
3) the electron and the antielectron
4) the electron-neutrino and the electron-antineutrino
5) the negative muon and the positive muon
6) the muon-neutrino and the muon-antineutrino

The leptons pose physicists some problems. Does the graviton really exist? Why does the muon exist; what is the purpose of something that is just a heavy electron? Why and how are the muon-neutrinos different from the electron-neutrinos?

These puzzles are intriguing but they don't drive physicists to despair.

In 1947, only three particles were coming to be known which would now be considered mesons. Two of them were the positive pion and the negative antipion. The third was a neutral pion which, like the photon and the graviton, was its own antiparticle.

Only four particles were known in 1947 that would now be classified as baryons. These are the proton, antiproton, neutron, and antineutron. Both antiproton and antineutron had not yet actually been detected, but physicists were quite sure they existed.

The situation with regard to the nucleus seemed particularly well settled. There was the nucleus made up of protons and neutrons held together by pions, and the antinucleus made up of antiprotons and antineutrons held together by antipions. All seemed well.

But in 1947, the very year which saw the discovery of the pion and the apparent solution of the problem of the nucleus, there began a new series of discoveries that upset the applecart again.

Two English physicists, George Dixon Rochester and Clifford Charles Butler, studying cosmic rays with cloud chambers in 1947, came across an odd V-shaped track. It was as though some neutral particle, which left no track, had suddenly broken into two particles, which each had a charge and left a track, and which hastened away in different directions.

The particle that moved off in one direction and formed one branch of the V seemed to be a pion, but the other was something new. From the nature of the track it left, it seemed to be as massive as a thousand electrons, or as three and a half pions. It was half as massive as a proton.

Nothing like such a particle had ever been suspected of existing. It caught the world of physicists by surprise, and at first all that could be done was to give it a name. It was called a "V-particle," and the collision that produced it was a "V-event."

Once physicists became aware of V-events, they began to watch for them and, of course, soon discovered additional ones. By 1950, V-particles were found which seemed to be actually more massive than protons or neutrons. This was another shock. Somehow physicists had taken it for granted that protons and neutrons were the most massive particles there were.

The astonished physicists began to study the new particles carefully. The first V-particle to be discovered, the one that was only half as massive as a proton, was found to have certain properties much like those of the pion. The new particle was therefore classified as a meson. It was called a "K-meson" and the name was quickly abbreviated to "kaon." There were four of these: a positive kaon, a negative antikaon, a neutral kaon, and a neutral antikaon.

The other V-particles discovered in the early 1950s were all more massive than the proton and were grouped together as "hyperons." There were three kinds of these and each kind was given the name of a Greek letter. The lightest were the "lambda particles," which were about 20 percent heavier than protons. These came in two varieties, a lambda and an anti-lambda, both of them uncharged.

Next lightest were the "sigma particles," which were nearly 30 percent heavier than the proton. There was a positive sigma, a negative, and a neutral, and each had its antiparticle. That meant six sigma particles altogether.

Finally, there were the "xi particles," which were 40 percent heavier than the proton. There was a negative xi particle and a neutral one (no positive variety) and each had its antiparticle, making four altogether.

All these hyperons, an even dozen of them, had many properties that resembled those of the proton and neutron. They were therefore lumped with them as baryons. Whereas there had been four baryons known, or suspected, in 1947, there were sixteen in 1957.

But then things grew rapidly more complicated still. Partly, it was because physicists were building machines capable of producing particles with more and more energy. This meant that nuclei were being smashed into with greater and greater force and it was possible to turn the energy into all sorts of particles.

What's more, physicists were developing new and better means of detecting particles. In 1952, a young American physicist, Donald Arthur Glaser, got an idea for something that turned out to be better than the cloud chamber. It was, in fact, rather the reverse of the cloud chamber.

A cloud chamber contains gas that is on the point of turning partly liquid. Charged particles, racing through, help the liquid to form and leave trails of water droplets.

But suppose it were the reverse. Suppose there was a chamber which contained liquid that was on the point of boiling and turning into gas. Charged particles passing through the liquid would form ions. The liquid immediately around the ion would boil with particular ease and form small bubbles of gas. The tracks would be gas bubbles in liquid, instead of liquid drops in gas.

This new kind of detecting device was called a "bubble chamber."

The advantage of a bubble chamber is that the liquid it contains is much denser than the air in a cloud chamber. There are more atoms and molecules in the liquid for a flying particle to collide with. More ions are formed and a clearer trail is left behind. Particles that could scarcely be seen in a cloud chamber are seen very clearly in a bubble chamber.

By using bubble chambers and finding many more kinds of

tracks, physicists began to suspect, by 1960, that there were certain particles that came into existence very briefly. They were never detected but unless they existed there was no way of explaining the tracks that were detected.

These new particles were very short-lived indeed. Until now the most unstable particles that had been detected lasted for a billionth of a second or so. That was a long enough time for them to make visible tracks in a bubble chamber.

The new particles, however, broke down in something like a hundred thousandth of a billionth of a billionth of a second. In that time, the particle has only a chance to travel about the width of a nucleus before breaking down.

These new particles were called "resonance particles" and different varieties have been deduced in great numbers since 1960. By now there are over a hundred baryons known that are heavier than protons. The heaviest are over twice as massive as protons.

Some of the new particles are mesons, all of them heavier than the pion. There are about sixty of these.

In the 1960s then, physicists were faced with the problem of finding some way of accounting for a large number of massive particles for which they could think of no uses and whose existence they couldn't predict.

At first all that physicists could do was to study the way in which one particle broke down into another; or the way in which one particle was built up into another when energy was added. Some changes could take place, while some changes could not. Particle A might change into particles B and C, but never into particles D and E.

Physicists tried to work out rules which would explain why some changes could take place and some could not. For instance, a neutron couldn't change into only a proton, because the proton has a positive electric charge and that can't be made out of nothing.

A neutron might, however, change into a proton plus an electron. In that case, a positive and a negative charge would be formed simultaneously. Together, they might be considered as balancing each other, so it would be as though no charge at all were formed.

But then to balance certain other qualities, such as the particle spin, more was required. In the end, it turned out that a neutron had to break down to three particles: a proton, an electron, and an antineutrino.

Matters such as electric charge and particle spin were enough to explain the events that were known in the old days when only a dozen or so different particles were known. In order to explain all the events that took place among nearly 200 particles, more rules had to be worked out. Quantities such as "isotopic spin," "hypercharge," "parity," and so on, had to be taken into account.

There is even something called "strangeness." Every particle is given a "strangeness number" and if this is done correctly, it turns out that whenever one group of particles changes into another group, the total strangeness number isn't altered.

The notion of strangeness made it plainer that there were actually two kinds of nuclear forces. The one that had first been proposed by Yukawa and that involved pions was an extremely strong one. In the course of the 1950s, however, it became clear that there was also a much weaker nuclear force, only about a hundred trillionths as strong as the strong one.

Changes that took place under the influence of the strong nuclear force took place extremely rapidly—just long enough to allow a resonance particle to break down. Changes that took place under the influence of the weak nuclear force took much longer—at least a billionth of a second or so.

Only the baryons and the mesons could take part in strong-force changes. The leptons took part only in weak-force changes. The baryons and mesons are therefore lumped together sometimes as "hadrons."

Even when physicists gradually worked out the rules that showed what particle changes could take place and what couldn't take place, they were very unsatisfied. They didn't understand why there should be so *many* particles.

More and more physicists began to wonder if the actual number of particles was unimportant. Perhaps particles existed in families and they ought to concentrate on families of particles.

For instance, the first two baryons discovered were the proton and the neutron. They seemed two completely different particles because there was an important unlikeness about them. The proton had a positive electric charge and the neutron had no electric charge at all.

This seemed to be an enormous difference. Because of it, a proton could be detected easily in a cloud chamber and a neutron couldn't. Because of it a proton followed a curved path when brought near a magnet but a neutron didn't.

And yet when the strong nuclear force was discovered, it was found that it affected protons and neutrons exactly the same, as though there were no difference between them. If the proton and neutron are considered from the standpoint of the strong nuclear force only, they are twins.

Could it be, then, that we ought to consider the proton and neutron as two forms of a single particle which we might call the "nucleon" (because it is found in the nucleus)? Certainly, that might simplify matters.

You can see what this means if you consider people. Certainly, a husband and a wife are two different people, very different in important ways. To the income tax people, however, they are just one tax-paying combination when they file a joint return. It doesn't matter whether the husband makes the money, or the wife, or both make half; in the return it is all lumped together. For tax purposes we simply have a tax-payer in two different forms, husband and wife.

After 1960, when the resonance particles began to turn up, physicists began to think more and more seriously of particle families. In 1961, two physicists, Murray Gell-Mann in the United States and Yuval Ne'eman in Israel, working sepa-rately, came up with very much the same scheme for forming particle families.

To do this, one had to take all the various particle proper-ties that physicists had worked out and arrange them in a very regular way. There were eight different kinds of properties that Gell-Mann worked with in order to set up a family pat-tern. Jokingly, he called his system the "Eightfold Way," after a phrase in the teachings of the Indian religious leader Buddha. The more formal name of his scheme is "SU(3) symmetry."

In what turned out to be the most famous example of SU(3) symmetry, Gell-Mann prepared a family of ten particles.

This family of ten can be pictured as follows. Imagine a triangle made up of four objects at the bottom, three objects above them, two objects above them, and one object all by itself at the apex.

The four objects at the bottom are four related "delta par-ticles" each about 30 percent heavier than a proton. The chief difference among them is the electric charge. The four delta particles have charges of −1, 0, +1, and +2.

Above these are three "sigma particles" more massive than the deltas and with charges of −1, 0, and +1. Above that are two "xi particles," which are still more massive and which have charges of −1, and 0. Finally, at the apex of the triangle is a single particle that is most massive of all and that has a charge of −1. Gell-Mann called this last particle the "omega-minus" particle, because "omega" is the last letter in the Greek alphabet and because the particle has a negative electric charge.

Notice that there is a regular way in which mass goes up and the number of separate particles goes down. Notice also that there is a regular pattern to the electric charges: -1, 0, $+1$, $+2$ for the first set; then -1, 0, $+1$; then -1, 0; finally -1.

Other properties also change in a regular way from place to place in the pattern. The whole thing is very neat indeed.

There was just one problem. Of the ten particles in this family, only nine were known. The tenth particle, the omega-minus at the apex, had never been observed. If it did not exist the whole pattern was ruined. Gell-Mann suggested that it did exist; that if people looked for it and knew exactly what they were looking for, they would find it.

If Gell-Mann's pattern was correct, one ought to be able to work out all the properties of the omega-minus by taking those values that would fit into the pattern. When this was done, it was found that the omega-minus would have to be a most unusual particle for some of its properties were like nothing yet seen.

For one thing, if it were to fit into its position at the top of the triangle it would have to have an unusual strangeness number. The deltas at the bottom of the triangle had a strangeness number of 0, the sigmas above them a strangeness number of -1, and the xis above them one of -2. The omega-minus particle at the top would therefore have to have a strangeness number of -3. No strangeness number that large had ever been encountered and physicists could scarcely bring themselves to believe that one would be.

Nevertheless, they began to search for it.

The instrument for the purpose was at Brookhaven, where, as the 1960s opened, an enormous new device for speeding particles was put into operation. It could speed up particles to the point where they would possess energies as high as 33

Bev. This was more than five times the quantity of energy that was enough to produce antiprotons some years before.

In November 1963, this instrument was put to work in the search for the omega-minus particle. Along with it was a new bubble chamber that contained liquid hydrogen. Hydrogen was liquid only at very frigid temperatures, hundreds of degrees below the ordinary zero.

The advantage to the use of liquid hydrogen was that hydrogen nuclei were made up of single protons (except for the very rare deuterium form of the element). Nothing else could supply so many protons squeezed into so small a space without any neutrons present to confuse matters.

The liquid hydrogen bubble chamber was nearly seven feet across and contained over 900 quarts of liquid hydrogen. There would be very little that would escape it.

Physicists had to calculate what kind of particle collisions might possess sufficient energy plus all the necessary properties to form an omega-minus particle, if one could be formed at all. You would have to have a collision that would supply the necessary strangeness number of -3, for instance. It would also have to be a collision that would supply no quantity of something called "isotopic spin," for the isotopic spin of omega-minus would have to be 0 if it were to fit Gell-Mann's pattern.

It was finally decided that what was needed was to smash high-energy negative kaons into protons. If everything went right, an occasional collision should produce a proton, a positive kaon, a neutral kaon, and an omega-minus particle.

A beam of 5 Bev negative kaons was therefore shot into the liquid hydrogen bubble chamber and by January 30, 1964, fifty thousand photographs had been taken. Nothing unusual was found in any of them.

On January 31, however, a photograph appeared in which a series of tracks were produced which seemed to indicate that an omega-minus particle had been formed and had broken down to form other particles. If certain known and easily recognized particles were followed backward, and it were calculated what kind of particles they must have come from, and then those were followed backward, one reached the very brief existence of an omega-minus particle.

A few weeks later, another photograph showed a different combination of tracks which could be worked backward to an omega-minus particle.

In other words, a particle had been detected which had broken down in two different ways. Both breakdown routes were possible for the omega-minus particle if it had exactly the properties predicted by Gell-Mann. Since then, a number of other omega-minus particles have been detected, all with exactly the predicted properties.

There seemed no question about it. The omega-minus particle did exist. It had never been detected because it was formed so rarely and existed so briefly. Now that physicists had been told exactly what to look for and where to look for it, however, they had found it.

Physicists are now satisfied that they must deal with particle families. There are arguments as to exactly how to arrange these families, of course, but that will probably be straightened out.

But can matters become simpler still? It has often happened in the history of science that when matters seemed to grow very complicated, it could all be made simpler by some basic discovery.

For instance, there are uncounted millions of different kinds of materials on Earth, but chemists eventually found they were all formed out of a hundred or so different kinds of elements, and that all the elements were made up, in the main, of three kinds of particles: protons, neutrons, and electrons.

In the twentieth century, as physicists looked more and more closely at these subatomic particles and found that nearly two hundred of them existed altogether, naturally they began to think of going deeper still. What lies beyond the protons and neutrons?

It is a case of digging downward into the littler and littler and littler. First to atoms, then beyond that to the nucleus, then beyond that to the proton and neutron, and now beyond that to—what?

Gell-Mann, in working out his family patterns, found that he could arrange them by letting each particle consist of three different symbols in different combinations. He began to wonder if these different symbols were just mathematical conveniences or if they were real objects.

For instance, you can write one dollar as $1.00, which is the same as writing 100¢. This would make it seem that there are one hundred cents in a dollar, and there certainly are. But does this mean that if you were to take a paper dollar bill and tear it carefully apart you would find a hundred one-cent pieces in it? Of course not!

The question was, then, if you tore a proton apart, would you find the three smaller objects that represented the three symbols used by Gell-Mann.

Gell-Mann decided to give the particles a name at least. He happened to think of a passage in *Finnegan's Wake* by James Joyce. This is a very difficult book in which words are deliberately twisted so as to give them more than one meaning. The passage he thought of was a sentence that went "Three quarks for Muster Mark."

Since three of these simple particles were needed for each of the different baryons, Gell-Mann decided, in 1963, to call them "quarks."

If the quarks were to fit the picture, they would have to have some very amazing properties. The most amazing was that they would have to have fractional electric charges.

When the electron was first discovered, its electric charge was set at -1 for simplicity's sake. Since then, all new particles discovered have either no electric charge at all or have one that is exactly equal to that of the electron or to an exact multiple of that charge. The same held for positive charges.

In other words, particles can have charges of 0, −1, +1, −2, +2, and so on. What has never been observed has been any fractional charge. No particle has ever yet been found to have a charge of +1½ or −2⅕.

Yet a fractional charge was exactly what the quarks would have to have. Charges of −⅓ and +⅔ would have to be found among them.

An immense search is now on for the quarks, for if they are found, they will simplify the physicist's picture of the structure of matter a great deal.

There is one important difficulty. Gell-Mann's theory makes it quite plain that when quarks come together to form ordinary subatomic particles, the process gives off a great deal of energy. In fact, almost all the mass of the quarks is given off as energy and only about one-thirtieth is left to form the particle. This means that quarks are thirty times as massive as the particles they produce.

(This sounds strange, but think about it. Suppose you see three balloons blown up almost to bursting. Would you suppose it were possible to squeeze them into a small box just an inch long in each direction? All you would have to do would be to let the air out of the balloons and what is left can easily be packed away in a small box. Similarly, when three quarks combine, you "let the mass out" and what is left can easily fit into a proton.)

If you want to form a quark by breaking apart a proton or some other particle, then you have to supply all the energy that the quarks gave up in the first place. You have to supply enough energy to form a group of particles thirty times as massive as a proton. You would need at least fifteen times as much energy as was enough to form a proton and antiproton in the 1950s, and probably even more.

There is no instrument on Earth, not even Brookhaven's 33-Bev colossus, that can supply the necessary energy.

Physicists have two things they can do. First, they can turn to the astronomers and ask them to watch for any sign of quarks in outer space. There are cosmic ray particles with sufficient energy to form quarks. Most cosmic ray particles are protons and if two of them smash together hard enough they may chip themselves into quarks.

However, this would happen very rarely and so far astronomers have detected nothing they could identify as quarks.

The second possibility is to build a device that will produce particles with sufficient energy to form quarks. In January 1967, the government of the United States announced plans to build such an instrument in Weston, Illinois.

This will be a huge device, nearly a mile across. It will take six or seven years to build and will cost 375 million dollars. Once it is completed, it will cost 60 million dollars a year to run.

But when it is done, physicists hope it will produce streams of particles with energies up to 200 Bev. This may be enough to produce quarks—or to show that they probably don't exist.

Physicists are awaiting the completion of the new instrument with considerable excitement and the rest of us should be excited, also. So far, every new advance in the study of the atom has meant important discoveries for the good of mankind.

By studying atoms in the first place, chemists learned to put together a variety of dyes and medicines, fertilizers and explosives, alloys and plastics that had never existed in nature.

By digging inside the atom and studying the electron, physicists made possible the production of such devices as radio and television.

The study of the atomic nucleus gave us the various nuclear bombs. These are not very pleasant things, to be sure, but the same knowledge also gave us nuclear power stations. It may make possible the production of so much cheap energy that our old planet may possibly reach toward a new era of comfort and ease.

Now physicists are trying to find the quarks that lie beyond the subatomic particle. We can't predict what this will result in, but it seems certain there will be results that may change the world even more than plastics, and television, and atomic power.

We will have to wait and see. Once the new device is put into action at Weston, it is just possible we may not have to wait long.

4—A NEW LOOK AT THE PLANETS

The study of the planets reached a peak in the nineteenth century and then, toward its end, seemed to die down. Other subjects began to interest astronomers much more. There was nothing left, it would appear, for twentieth century astronomers to do about planets.

If, indeed, the planets seemed worked out by 1900, that is not surprising. After all, astronomers had been dealing with them for over 2,000 years, and what more could be left?

To be sure, the ancients had gotten off on the wrong foot. The Greeks had worked out careful and interesting theories concerning the motions of the planets as early as 350 B.C. They thought, however, that all the planets revolved about the Earth.

In 1543, the Polish astronomer Nicolaus Copernicus published a book which argued that the planets revolved about the sun. He also insisted that the Earth was one of the planets, too, and that it also revolved about the sun. (The moon, however, revolved about the Earth in the new system as well as the old.)

In 1609, the German astronomer Johannes Kepler worked out the fact that the planets revolved about the sun in ellipses, which resembled slightly flattened circles. Then, in 1683, the

English scientist Isaac Newton showed how the sun and its planets (the solar system) were held together by gravitational force. All the motions of the planets could be worked out quite accurately by means of a clear formula which Newton presented.

Meanwhile in 1609, the Italian astronomer Galileo Galilei had devised a small telescope which he pointed at the heavens. At once, he saw numerous things no one had ever seen before. He discovered that there were spots on the sun, for instance, and that there were mountains on the moon. He also found that Jupiter had four moons that moved about it just as our moon goes about the Earth.

For a hundred and fifty years after Newton, astronomers worked hard to make new discoveries about the solar system with ever-improving telescopes. They showed more and more of its workings to be explained by Newton's simple law of gravitation.

New bodies were discovered. Saturn was found to have moons like Jupiter. It was found to have rings, thin circles of light, about its equator. Even a new planet was discovered in 1781 by the German-English astronomer William Herschel. It was found to circle the sun at a distance far beyond Saturn and it was named Uranus.

The climax of all this came in the middle of the nineteenth century. The motions of Uranus about the sun had been followed for over half a century and they did not quite follow Newton's law. This was very puzzling and upsetting to the astronomers of the time.

One or two of them wondered if there might not be a planet beyond Uranus; one that had not yet been discovered. Perhaps this unknown planet was exerting a gravitational pull on Uranus, a pull that wasn't being taken into account.

In 1845, two young astronomers actually tried to calculate where such a planet ought to be located if it were to produce just enough effect to make Uranus move as it did. One was an

Englishman, John Couch Adams, and the other a Frenchman, Urbain Jean Joseph Leverrier. Neither knew the other was working on the problem, but both ended with just about the same answer.

When telescopes were turned on the spot where they said the planet ought to be, it was found! It was a new giant planet far beyond Uranus and it was given the name Neptune.

It was the greatest triumph in the history of astronomy and the great climax of the study of the solar system. There seemed nothing left to do among the planets that could possibly equal the drama of 1845.

This seemed all the more true as by the middle of the nineteenth century, the solar system was beginning to seem a small and insignificant thing anyway. Astronomers' attention was beginning to switch more and more to the distant stars.

In the 1830s, they had developed methods for determining the distance of the nearer stars. By 1860, methods were devised to analyze starlight. Astronomers could tell how hot a star was, whether it was moving toward us or away from us, even the materials of which it was made.

With all these exciting discoveries being made about the stars, fewer and fewer astronomers were left to concern themselves with the little worlds of our own sun's family.

The solar system wasn't entirely deserted, of course. Some new discoveries were made that were pretty exciting.

In 1877, for instance, Mars and Earth happened to be in those parts of their orbits that brought them only thirty-five million miles apart. That is as close together as they ever get. With Mars that close, the American astronomer Asaph Hall discovered that it possessed two tiny moons.

At the same time, an Italian astronomer, Giovanni Virginio Schiaparelli, found straight dark markings on Mars, which he called "canali" an Italian word for "channels." The word was mistranslated into English as "canals."

This made a great difference. Channels are merely narrow

bodies of water, but canals are man-made. If Mars had "canals" that would mean there was intelligent life on it. Naturally, this excited people and there was considerable discussion about it in the newspapers.

Astronomers, however, did not get overly excited about the matter. Most of them couldn't see the markings that Schiaparelli had seen, and they suspected that even if they did, there was bound to be some explanation for it other than the presence of intelligent life.

As the twentieth century opened, however, one man brought the question of the canals to the fore. He was an American astronomer named Percival Lowell, who came of an old Boston family and had considerable money.

Using his private fortune, Lowell built an elaborate astronomical observatory in Arizona where the clean desert air and the absence of clouds made it easy to observe the heavens. This observatory was opened in 1894 and for fifteen years Lowell concentrated on watching Mars.

He was sure that Mars was covered with a fine network of straight lines. He made elaborate maps of these lines and was convinced they were indeed the work of intelligent beings. Many people who weren't astronomers were convinced by him. Most astronomers, however, remained skeptical. They insisted that whatever Lowell saw must be optical illusions.

Lowell created a stir in another direction as well. He was not satisfied that Neptune was indeed the farthest planet from the sun. Even after Neptune's gravitational pull was taken into account, Uranus still didn't travel in quite the path one would consider correct from gravitational theory.

Lowell insisted there was yet another planet beyond Neptune and that it, too, pulled on Uranus—though more weakly because it was farther away. He searched and searched for this "Planet X" but when he died in 1916, he had not yet found it.

The trouble is that the more distant a planet, the smaller

and dimmer it appears and the harder it is to distinguish it from the stars that can be seen at the same time. Planet X was probably so far away that a telescope good enough to see it would also make out crowds of faint stars. The problem would then become that of telling one dot of light which was a planet from a million other dots of light which were stars.

Even if calculations were to tell an astronomer about where such a planet might be, it would still have to be picked out from among the many stars in the same neighborhood.

After Lowell died, the observatory he had built kept on going and occasionally astronomers who worked there would do a bit of looking for Planet X. In 1929, the search went back into high gear when a twenty-three-year-old youngster, Clyde William Tombaugh, joined the staff.

Tombaugh's family were poor farmers who could not afford to send their son to college. Tombaugh, however, was fascinated by astronomy. He read all he could on the subject and when he was twelve years old he even built a small telescope for himself out of material he managed to get his hands on. By the time he was twenty, he had built a neat nine-inch telescope that worked very well indeed.

With his homemade telescope he studied Mars and managed to observe a few canals now and then. He grew interested, wrote to Lowell Observatory in the hope of getting a job, and got one.

Tombaugh set to work searching for Planet X. It might be just a point of light (if it were there) like any star, but it was different from a star in one important way. Planet X moved about the sun and that meant that it shifted its position in space.

Planet X was very far from the sun, of course, so that it moved slowly. That slow motion was even slower in appearance to astronomers on Earth because the planet was so far away. Even so, the motion could be spotted easily after two or three days in comparison with the surrounding stars, which didn't move at all!

Tombaugh's technique, then, was to take a photograph of a particular tiny portion of the sky. Then, two or three days later, that same tiny portion of the sky would be photographed again. If the only thing on the photographs were stars then nothing at all would have changed position in the slightest. All Tombaugh would have to do would be to check whether any of the tiny star-images on one plate was in a different position when compared to the other.

That was easier said than done. Each photograph contained, on the average, 160,000 stars, and it was just impractical to go over all of them. It would take too much time, and, unless Tombaugh had a tremendous stroke of luck, the chance of finding Planet X would be very small.

But Tombaugh did the following. The two photographic plates were placed side by side under a kind of viewer through which Tombaugh could look and see only one. He could adjust a tiny mirror that would enable him to see first the photograph on the left, then the one on the right.

He could adjust the two photographs so that both would be in exactly the same position. Then, if he flipped the lever that adjusted the mirror, he would view the photographs left, right, left, right, left, right, over and over. If both were properly adjusted, the photographs would be so alike that he wouldn't be able to tell them apart.

But if Planet X were somewhere on the plate, it would change position, for it would have moved during the several days between the taking of the first photograph and the second. As Tombaugh flipped the lever, the image of Planet X would shift back and forth, back and forth. All he had to do then was to adjust the photographs, flip the lever, and watch for any point that blinked. He could ignore all the thousands upon thousands of other points.

Even that wasn't very easy. He had to study the plates one

tiny bit at a time. Sometimes he had to flip the photographs back and forth for six or seven hours before he could study all parts of them and be convinced that no point blinked. Then, too, sometimes there was a moving point but it was an asteroid, one of the tiny planets that moved about the sun between the orbits of Mars and Jupiter.

Such asteroids were much closer to the sun and to the Earth than Planet X was. This meant that they moved more quickly and that there was a much larger shift against the stars. If Tombaugh found a spot that moved too far, that was as bad as one that didn't move at all. It couldn't be Planet X.

In late January 1930, Tombaugh photographed the stars in a section of the constellation Gemini. For nearly a month he kept examining those photographs and on February 18, he caught a shift that was so small it had to be a very distant planet. For weeks he kept taking photographs of that spot and watching the way that the little dot moved until there was no doubt. The path of the object agreed with what would be expected of a planet beyond Neptune.

The discovery was announced on March 13, 1930, the day when Percival Lowell would have celebrated his seventy-fifth birthday if he had lived. The planet was named Pluto, partly because Pluto was the god of the dark underground in the Greek myths and the new planet was so far from the sun that it received less light than any other planet. Partly, also, the name was chosen because the first two letters were the initials of Percival Lowell.

At just about the time the discovery of the new planet Pluto was announced, astronomers were getting ready for a huge international project involving the solar system.

Ever since Kepler had worked out the elliptical orbits of the planets in 1609, astronomers had been able to draw an exact model of the solar system. What was lacking, though, was any notion of the actual size of this model. If only they could get the exact distance of any planet of the solar system, they could work out the distances of all the rest from the model.

The closest planets were Mars and Venus. Mars sometimes was as close as thirty-five million miles from the Earth and Venus was even closer, sometimes only twenty-five million miles away.

If either Mars or Venus were viewed at the same time from two widely separated observatories on Earth, the planet would be seen against two slightly different backgrounds. That is, it would be seen from two different angles against the stars.

From the distance between the two observatories and from the size of the shift in the position of the planet, the distance of the planet could be calculated. Then the distance of all the other planets could be calculated, too. In particular, the distance of the sun from the Earth could be calculated.

There were problems, though. When Venus was closest to the Earth, it was more or less between the sun and the Earth and it couldn't be seen. Sometimes Venus passes exactly between the sun and the Earth and then it can be seen as a dark spot against the sun's brightness. If the moment at which Venus moves in front of before the sun is measured from two widely separated observatories, then the distance of the planet can be calculated.

Unfortunately, these "transits" don't happen often. Not a single transit will take place in the twentieth century, for instance. Another problem is that Venus has a thick atmosphere, which blurs the exact moment at which it begins to move before the sun.

Mars makes a better target, therefore, even though it is farther away and never passes in front of the sun. Using Mars enabled astronomers were able to determine the size of the solar system pretty well. The distance of the sun was placed at somewhere between ninety-three and ninety-five million miles from the Earth.

Just the same, Mars has a thin atmosphere and it shows up as a small globe in the telescope so that its exact position is a little fuzzy. What is needed is a planet even closer than Mars or Venus and one that is so small it has no atmosphere and looks like a mere dot of light in the telescope.

Unfortunately, there is no such planet. Or is there?

Tiny planets do exist. There are the asteroids that circle in orbits between Mars and Jupiter. The largest is less than 500 miles in diameter (as compared with 8,000 miles for the Earth) and it was discovered on January 1, 1801. Most of those discovered afterward were less than 100 miles across and there may be many thousands that are only a couple of miles across and are too dim to see.

In 1896, a German astronomer, G. Witt, discovered a new asteroid, which happened to be number 433. Another new asteroid wasn't much, but when Witt came to calculate its orbit, in 1898, he received a shock. Unlike all the other asteroid orbits known, this new one slipped inward, so that much of the time the new asteroid was closer to the sun than Mars.

Ordinarily asteroids receive female names, but Witt named this one Eros, and ever since then asteroids with unusual orbits get male names.

The orbit of Eros is such that at long intervals it can approach the Earth much more closely than either Mars or Venus. In 1931, it was scheduled to pass within sixteen million miles of Earth, almost its minimum distance.

Astronomers thought it would be wonderful if Eros could be observed from different places. It was just a dot of light and would shift its position far more than either Mars or Venus. There would be no trouble making an accurate measurement of that shift.

The greatest international astronomical project ever attempted up to that time was set up. Fourteen observatories in nine different countries took part. Seven months were spent on the project and nearly three thousand photographs were taken. The position of Eros was carefully checked on each one of them.

It took ten years for the proper calculations to be made

under the supervision of the English astronomer Harold Spencer-Jones. Finally, the results were announced. The solar system had been cut to size more accurately than ever before. The average distance of the sun from the Earth was found to be 93,005,000 miles.

The twentieth century saw a number of discoveries of new small members of the solar system. When the century opened, only five satellites of Jupiter were known, but between 1904 and 1951 seven more were discovered. All were small and all were distant from Jupiter. Astronomers feel they are asteroids that had managed to move too close to Jupiter and had gotten caught in its gravitational field.

The planet Uranus had four known satellites and Neptune one in 1900, but in 1948, a fifth satellite of Uranus, smaller than the rest and closer to the planet than any of the others, was discovered by the Dutch-American astronomer Gerard Peter Kuiper. It was named Miranda. The next year, 1949, Kuiper also discovered a second satellite of Neptune. It was small and circled Neptune at a great distance. He named it Nereid.

Nine newly discovered satellites had thus joined the lists of known members of the solar system between 1900 and 1966, bringing the total number to 31.

Saturn was the only one of the outer planets to have received no addition to its satellite family. It had nine known satellites and the ninth, Phoebe, had been discovered in 1898 by the American astronomer William Henry Pickering. Now, nearly seventy years had passed and nothing new had been added. To be sure, in 1905, Pickering had reported a tenth, which he named Themis, but that seems to have been a mistake. No one has ever seen it since.

But Saturn has something other planets do not have. It has a set of thin, flat rings that circle the planet at its equator. They are composed of innumerable small fragments which may be no more than pebble-size and which may be largely ice.

Saturn's poles are tipped toward and away from the sun (just as Earth's poles are) and that means the rings are tipped, too. We see them either a little from above or a little from below, depending on where Earth and Saturn are in their orbits. Whether we see them from above or below the brightness of the rings makes it hard to see anything else that may be very near Saturn.

As Saturn's rings shift from a top view to a bottom view, however, there comes a short period, once every fourteen and a half years, in which we see the rings edge-on. The rings are so thin that they become invisible when seen from the edge and the area close to Saturn can then be studied.

In December 1966, the rings were edge-on and a French astronomer, Audoin Dollfuss, photographed the regions near the planet. He studied the photographs and was pleased to find a tenth satellite. It was closer to Saturn than any of the others and lay just outside the rings. Edge-on time was about the only moment when it could be seen easily. Because it was the first satellite, counting out from Saturn, and the last satellite to be discovered, Dollfuss named it Janus after the Roman god of first and last things.

New asteroids were also discovered in the twentieth century and some of them were even more remarkable than Eros.

In 1906, the German astronomer Max Wolf discovered the 588th asteroid. It was odd, indeed, for its orbit was almost exactly that of Jupiter. He therefore gave it the masculine name of Achilles. A whole group of asteroids has been found in Jupiter's orbit since then, some moving about 480 million miles behind Jupiter and some about 480 million miles ahead of it. (Gravitational theory explains that such a situation is a stable one.) They were all given names of characters from Homer's poem about Troy and are called the "Trojan asteroids."

In 1920, the German astronomer Walter Baade discovered what is, even today, the farthest of all known asteroids. Its orbit carries it far beyond Jupiter and takes it nearly as far from the sun as Saturn. He named it Hidalgo.

Then in 1948, Baade (who by now had become an American citizen) discovered the satellite that approaches most closely to the sun. This is Icarus (named after a character in the Greek myths who flew through the air on feathered wings held together by wax but who flew so close to the sun that the wax melted so that he dropped to his death). Icarus approaches within seventeen million miles of the sun. This is considerably closer than the approach of Mercury, the innermost large planet.

The orbit of Icarus is such that it can approach within four million miles of Earth. This is a much closer approach than even that of Eros, so that Icarus is one of the group of asteroids now called "Earth-grazers." About half a dozen of these are now known, most having been discovered in the 1930s.

In 1937, the German astronomer Karl Reinmuth detected an asteroid which he named Hermes. Its orbit, when calculated, showed that it could approach as closely as 200,000 miles. It would then be even closer than the moon.

Yet none of all these discoveries of the first thirty years of the twentieth century seemed to make the solar system very exciting.

They lacked drama. The discovery of Pluto was the result of years of hard work, instead of the product of one great stroke. The work on Eros just resulted in a slight adjustment of the calculated distance of the sun. The discovery of a few small satellites and asteroids didn't seem like much.

The great excitement was going on far beyond the solar system. It was found that all the hundred billion stars of the Milky Way (of which the sun is one) make up a huge collection called the galaxy. Far outside that collection are many millions of other galaxies.

In the 1920s, moreover, it was discovered that the distant galaxies were moving away from us. The farther away they were, the faster they were moving. The whole universe was expanding.

It was a brand-new vision of endless space that broke on the eyes of the astronomers as the twentieth century progressed. There seemed little to compare with that in the solar system.

There were some interesting puzzles in the solar system, to be sure. There was still the question of canals on Mars. Were those marks really canals? Was there intelligent life on Mars? What lay under the mysterious blanket of clouds that hid the surface of Venus? What was on the other side of the moon, the side men never saw.

These were fascinating problems because they involved bodies that were so close to us, but there was no way astronomers could answer them. It seemed there would never be any way.

Yet although astronomers didn't realize it at the time, the 1920s and 1930s saw two enormous breakthroughs which were to revolutionize completely the study of the solar system in ways undreamed of in the nineteenth century.

One of these breakthroughs took place in 1926, when a professor at Clark University in Worcester, Massachusetts, fired a rocket into the air. This event, and what followed, will be considered in the next chapter. The other event, which took place in early 1932, will be described now.

One of the problems that faces astronomers is the fact that the Earth has an atmosphere. Naturally, people need the atmosphere to breathe; even astronomers do. But it is a problem when it comes to observing the heavens.

The atmosphere absorbs some of the light from the stars

and planets. It curves the light that reaches it from objects near the horizon and makes those objects appear higher in the sky than they really are. There are temperature differences that cause light beams to waver, so that it is hard to get sharp pictures. There is often haze and smoke in the air and sometimes clouds that blank out everything.

Then, too, as human population grows, cities grow too and become more and more lit up at night. This light is scattered by the air and it becomes harder than ever to watch the sky. Astronomers can scarcely find sites high enough on the mountains and far enough from cities to make it possible to observe the skies in peace.

But need astronomers be confined to studying the sky by ordinary light?

Ordinary light is only a small section of a huge band of radiation, and it seems quite likely that stars and planets send out other radiations in this band. Unfortunately, the other sections of the band of radiation can't be detected by eye so that special instruments are needed to receive them. Furthermore, Earth's atmosphere, which lets ordinary visible light through, stops most other sections of the radiation band cold.

All these different types of radiation, including visible light, act as though they are made up of tiny waves. The difference between one type of radiation and another is in the size of these waves. When the waves are very long, we have what we call "radio waves." These were discovered in 1888 by a German physicist, Heinrich Rudolf Hertz.

Whereas the waves of ordinary light are so short that there are about 50,000 to the inch, the individual radio wave can be many miles long. Even the shortest radio waves (called "microwaves") can be several inches long.

Once radio waves were discovered, physicists began to try to use them to carry signals over long distances. The Italian engineer, Guglielmo Marconi, managed to send signals by radio waves from England to Newfoundland in 1901, and that can be considered the birth of our modern radio.

Marconi's achievement was puzzling in a way. Radio waves travel in straight lines while the surface of the round Earth curves. How can radio waves manage to go round the curve? It turned out that the radio waves used by Marconi bounce off layers of ions in the upper atmosphere and zigzag up and down as they cross the Atlantic.

This does not happen if the radio waves are too short. The microwaves, for instance, go shooting through the layers of ions in the upper air (the "ionosphere") without trouble. Signals carried by microwaves would not travel along the Earth's surface for more than a few miles.

As a result, engineers who worked with radio (and there were many of them during the 1910s and 1920s) worked with long radio waves. Short radio waves were ignored because they seemed useless. No one paid attention to the fact that if they could go through the atmosphere as easily as ordinary light did, that they might be useful to astronomers.

The man who first got a hint of that fact was Karl Jansky, a young American radio engineer, working for the Bell Telephone Laboratories. The people at Bell Telephone were interested in telephone conversations carried on over long distances with the help of radio waves. These were often interfered with by static and it was Jansky's job to try to pin down the causes of the static. Once the causes were known, the cures might be found.

Jansky, working in New Jersey, devised a large radio antenna which could be rotated to receive signals from any direction. When there was static, there were sure to be stray radio waves acting to produce it. Jansky's antenna could be rotated until the static was loudest and it would then be pointing to the source. If the source were known, then perhaps something could be done about it.

Jansky expected that a lot of the trouble arose from thunderstorms and the stray radio waves set up by the lightning. Sure enough, he did get a kind of crackling static from lightning, even when it was far off on the horizon, too far to see.

But then, in January 1932, he became aware of a faint hiss in his receivers, a sound quite unlike the lightning crackle. He might have thought it was just "noise" created by imperfections in his apparatus, but the hiss became louder and softer as he turned his antenna.

He found that the hiss was loudest in the direction of the sun. He wondered if he might be receiving radio waves from the sun.

If the sun had happened to have a great many sunspots at the time, the radio waves would indeed have been coming from the sun, for it was eventually discovered that the spots give rise to intense radio waves. In 1932, however, the sun was at a quiet period with few spots. It was producing very little in the way of radio waves.

Therefore as Jansky turned his antenna every day, he found that the spot from which the hiss was coming was not from the sun at all. In fact, it moved farther from the sun every day.

The sun moves slowly against the background of the stars (because the Earth, from which we watch the sun, is revolving about it so that we see the sun from a different angle every day) but the source of the hiss did not move. It remained at the same point in the constellation of Sagittarius.

Jansky realized he was getting radio waves not from the sun but from a different and possibly much more distant source. We now know he was getting it from the center of our galaxy.

Jansky reported his findings, but they did not make much of a splash. The kind of radio waves that Jansky had detected coming from outer space were just those short microwaves with which nobody did any work. There were no instruments available that could really handle it. Astronomers preferred to work in fields where they had the instruments.

They didn't seem to realize that they were ignoring something that was perhaps the greatest astronomical discovery of the twentieth century.

One youngster, in his twenties, was inspired by the report, however. He was Grote Reber. He built a device in the back yard of his home in Wheaton, Illinois. It was a curved reflector, thirty-one feet across, with which he received radio waves and reflected them into a detecting device at the center. He put his "radio telescope" to work in 1937 and became the world's first radio astronomer.

All through the years of World War II, Reber kept carefully noting the quantity of radio waves coming from different portions of the sky. He was able, in this way, to produce the first radio map of the sky. He was also able to detect a few places from which radio waves seemed to be coming in particularly great quantities. These were the first "radio sources."

What eventually saved the situation was that during the 1930s interest grew in another angle of radio.

You can tell a great deal about an object if you bounce radiation off it and study the reflection. If you reflect light waves from a chair, the nature of the reflection will tell you the chair's shape, size, position, distance, color, and so on.

Bats use sound waves for the purpose. Their squeaks are reflected by insects, twigs, and other objects and by listening to the echo, they can catch the insects or avoid the twigs. There are other examples of the same process.

Now suppose you wanted to detect an enemy airplane at night without letting the enemy pilot know he was detected. You could use a bright beam of ordinary light but the enemy would see it. Besides light is easily stopped by clouds, fog, mist, or smoke.

It would be much better to use some other form of radiation that he couldn't see and that would pass through clouds and other such obstructions. The longer the waves of the radiation, the better they would pass through clouds and the rest. If the waves were too long, however, there would be too much of a tendency for them to move around an object instead of being reflected by it.

It turned out that microwaves were just right. Their waves were long enough to go through clouds and short enough to be reflected by planes.

In Great Britain especially, methods were developed for sending out a tight beam of microwaves and receiving the echo. Then, from the echo, you could tell the position and distance (or "range") of the reflecting object, which could be an enemy plane. The device was called "radio detection and ranging" and this was abbreviated as ra. d. a. r., which became the word "radar." Radar wave has therefore become another name for microwave.

Great Britain developed radar just in time to have it take part in the Battle of Britain in 1940. The British could detect the German planes coming in over the Channel by night as well as by day and were always waiting for them in the proper place. Without radar, Britain might have lost the war.

The important thing to astronomers was this: In developing radar, engineers had to learn to handle microwaves. Once they developed instruments to do that, those same instruments could be used to detect microwaves from outer space.

What's more, Great Britain became aware of microwaves from outer space in the course of the war.

In February 1942, Great Britain found severe interference with its radar network. The first thought was that the Germans had discovered the network and were jamming it in preparation for large new air strikes. A team under the British engineer Stanley Hey began to investigate the matter.

Hey discovered the source of the jamming in a few days. The sun was not quiet, as it had been when Jansky made his key discovery. It was loaded with sunspots and it was broadcasting radio waves. For the first time, radio waves from outer space were pinned down to a definite source—the sun.

Immediately after the war, astronomers, using all the equipment and techniques worked out through radar developments, turned to the study of radio astronomy in a big way.

The "radio sky" was mapped in greater and greater detail, and certain radio sources were identified. It was found that stars that had once exploded were such strong sources of radio waves that they could be detected through all the vast distances that separated those stars from us.

Indeed, it was discovered that whole galaxies could be sources of radio waves of even greater intensities. Distant galaxies could be detected with greater ease by radio telescopes than by ordinary ones.

Radio astronomy in the 1960s uncovered mysterious objects which were named "quasars" by astronomers. There is no certainty as to exactly what they are, but some think that they are small but enormously bright objects farther away than anything else we know. The quasars may tell us a great deal about the youth of the universe billions of years ago, and about its edges billions of trillions of miles away.

In fact, in 1964, certain types of radio waves were studied which seemed to come from all directions and which some astronomers think is the radiation that was released when our universe was first formed.

Interestingly enough, the great discoveries of radio astronomy were not confined to far away places only. News was brought to mankind concerning its nearest neighbors in space, the planets of the solar system. Some of the news was so exciting and unexpected that the study of the planets, which seemed to have been played out, suddenly burst out into fascinating new directions.

For instance, if beams of microwaves can be reflected from enemy aircraft, and if the echoes can give us information, why can't such beams be reflected from objects of astronomical interest.

Hey, who discovered the radio wave radiation of the sun during the war, also noted certain echoes that seemed to be originating in the upper atmosphere. From the time it took the echoes to return, he could calculate the height, and he began to wonder if he weren't detecting meteors.

After the war, he studied these echoes in detail. Finally, in 1946, he was able to show that meteors leave so thick a trail of ions that some microwaves are reflected. One could therefore study meteor trails by radar.

This was useful, for only the larger meteors (about the size of pinheads or more) could be seen by their gleaming light, as friction with the air heated them white-hot, and even then they could only be seen at night. Using radar, however, small meteors could be detected day or night, if they were in sufficiently large clusters.

Certain large clusters of meteors move around the sun in what had once been the orbits of comets that had finally fallen apart. Once a year, the Earth will pass through a particular cloud and there will then be a shower of flashing trails left by many meteors moving quickly through the atmosphere.

Once in a longish while the Earth may move through the thickest part of such a cloud and then the trails may appear to be as thick as snowflakes. This happened over the eastern United States in November 1833.

There are about a dozen meteor clouds that have been observed in this way. Now that radar observations are made, at least three more have been found that always strike from the general direction of the sun. They always approach on the daylight side of the Earth, in other words, and can never be seen by eye.

But do we have to confine ourselves to Earth's atmosphere? Could not a beam of microwaves travel outside the air altogether? If it were aimed in the direction of the moon, it could reach the moon in one and one-quarter seconds, strike its surface, bounce off, and shoot back. The echo would reach Earth again after another one and one-quarter seconds. There would be two and a half seconds altogether between the time of sending and the time of return.

Naturally, the radar beam would spread out with distance. Some of it would be absorbed by the moon. Some of it would bounce off in directions away from the Earth. Then the returning echo would spread out again over the distance between moon and Earth. Only a very faint echo would be received.

To detect such a faint echo, either a very intense beam must be sent out in the first place, or very sensitive devices must be developed for detecting echoes or both.

Difficult as it was, the feat was accomplished almost as soon as the end of World War II freed radar equipment for the task. In early 1946, a Hungarian, Zoltan Lajos Bay, (who has since emigrated to the United States) reported receiving echoes. A very short time afterward, the United States Army, with more powerful equipment, managed to do the job in an even more clear-cut way.

Reaching the moon by microwave was comparatively easy, because it is so close as compared with other astronomical bodies. The sun is much farther away but it is a giant in size so that it offers a large target. In 1959 astronomers aimed a beam of microwaves at it and a group at Stanford University in California managed to get an echo back. The sun's own microwave radiations confused the echo, of course, but it could be made out.

The important target, however, was Venus. Venus was closer than the sun and echoes could be received from it much more sharply. Still, Venus was a much smaller body than the sun, a little smaller than the Earth, even. It made a tiny target in the heavens, and it would be a triumph, indeed, if a beam of microwaves could be made to strike Venus and return to Earth. The returning echo would be exceedingly feeble and to detect it would require the most delicate instruments and the most careful work.

If it could be done, however, a great deal could be gained. Scientists knew quite accurately how quickly a beam of microwaves traveled through space. It traveled at the speed of light which is a fraction over 186,282 miles per second. If one could measure the exact length of time it took for the microwaves to travel from Earth to Venus and back, one could calculate just how far Venus was at that moment.

Then all the other distances of the various bodies of the solar system could be calculated from that. In just a few days, the distance of the sun could be determined more accurately than through the entire ten-year project that involved the asteroid Eros.

Everyone was trying for the Venus echo and in 1961 three different American groups, one British group, and one Russian group all succeeded. Each calculated the distance of Venus and then of the sun. The best figures, obtained by a group from M.I.T., seem to show that the average distance of the sun from the Earth is about 92,955,600 miles. That is 50,000 miles closer than the results given by the Eros project.

After Venus was successfully touched, other planets were reached. In 1962, a Russian team made microwave contact with Mercury, a smaller and more distant target than Venus. In 1963, astronomers at the California Institute of Technology made contact with Mars. There have also been reports of contact with Jupiter, a planet more distant by far than any of the earlier targets, but this is still uncertain.

Microwave echoes can tell us far more than the distance of an object. It can tell us a great deal about the kind of surface that is reflecting the beam.

Suppose the microwaves were bouncing off a perfectly smooth sphere. Those waves that hit the exact center of the side of the sphere facing us would bounce back perfectly.

The echo would come back right on the line along which the original wave had approached. The echo would return to the instrument that had sent out the wave and it would be detected.

Microwaves that hit the sphere a little away from the center of the side facing us would bounce off to one side. (You can see why this would be so if you imagined yourself throwing a ball at a curved wall. If the ball hit the wall where it curved away from you, it would bounce to one side.) The farther from the center that the radar touched, the farther to the side it would bounce.

But, of course, the moon is not a perfectly smooth sphere. It is uneven. It has mountains and craters, hills and rocks. A microwave striking the center of the moon might hit the side of a hill or even the side of a rock and be reflected away from us, instead of coming straight back.

Then, too, if a microwave struck a point on the moon quite a bit away from the center, it might hit an uneven portion slanted in such a way that the wave would be reflected right back to us. So you see we would be getting some echoes from all over the moon.

But the moon's surface curves away from us and near the rim of the part we can see, the surface is over a thousand miles farther from us than is the surface in the very center. This means that the microwave echo isn't absolutely clean and sharp. The part reflected from the center of the moon comes back first and then small echoes come back from uneven surfaces a little farther along the curve of the moon, and then from uneven surfaces a little farther still, and so on.

The echo is a little fuzzier than the original wave. The fuzziness becomes greater or less as microwaves with different wavelengths are used, for the smaller the wavelength, the more the wave is affected by small unevennesses. From all this astronomers can get an idea of how rough the moon's surface is.

To work out the roughness of the moon's surface by "feeling" it with microwaves is exciting, but again Venus is much more important.

Venus is our nearest neighbor in space, next to the moon, but we know almost nothing about it. Its thick atmosphere is filled with clouds that never thin out. All we can see is the cloud layer so that Venus, in the telescope, looks like a shiny, white ball with no markings.

Microwaves can penetrate those clouds, though, and bounce off the rocky soil no one has ever seen. From the fuzziness of the echo, something can be worked out about the unevenness of that surface.

Late in 1965, for instance, it was decided that there were at least two huge mountain ranges on Venus. One of them runs from north to south for about 2,000 miles and is several hundred miles wide. The other is even larger and runs east and west. The two ranges are named for the first two letters of the Greek alphabet. They are the "Alpha Mountains" and the "Beta Mountains."

It is still uncertain as to how high these mountains are, but astronomers are using additional microwave measurements to work out a crude map of Venus—the map of a surface we have never seen.

Microwave measurements have also been used to test the roughness of Mars and by 1967 it was decided that Mars was about as rough as the Earth. This was a surprise, for studies by ordinary telescopes had made it seem that Mars was rather smooth.

It now seems that some Martian mountain peaks are as much as eight miles above the lowland depths. This is actually higher than Earth's mountain peaks, but then Mars has no ocean. If we measured the height of our mountains above our ocean bottom instead of above the top of the ocean water, some of our ranges would be over ten miles high.

Even that isn't all the information microwave echoes can give us.

Suppose that a microwave beam is reflected by a body that is turning on its axis, and suppose the body is turning from left to right as we look at it.

The part of the body at the left is turning along the curve of its surface, toward the middle, which is closer to us than any other part is. The part of the body at the left is coming toward us, in other words. The part of the body at the right is naturally turning away from us.

If the microwave beam hits the left side of the body, which is coming toward us, then the waves are squeezed together. Those parts of the echo that reach us from there have shorter waves than the original beam had. In the same way, the radar beam that hits the right side bounces back from a part that is moving away and its waves are pulled apart. That part of the echo has longer waves than the original.

From the way in which the lengths of the radar waves have stretched out and pushed together as compared with the original, astronomers can tell how fast the body is turning.

This can be tried on the moon. We know how fast it is turning. Microwave echoes give the right answer.

Astronomers were therefore confident they could try it on other bodies. What about Mercury, for instance? They thought they knew how fast Mercury rotated on its axis—once in eighty-eight days, exactly as long as it took to go around the sun once.

This is no coincidence. When a small body turns about a nearby large body, the gravitational force of the large body pulls some of the small body toward itself and makes a bulge in its direction. As the small body turns, this bulge is forced to remain pointing to the large body. It slips about the small body and as it does so, it sets up friction that slows down the rotation; just as the friction of a brake slows down a bicycle.

Finally, the small body slows its rotation till it is turning just once on its axis each time it moves around the big body. When this happens, the small body always turns the same side to the big body, so that the bulge is always in one place. There is no more friction.

The moon turns on its axis in just the time it takes to move once around the Earth so it always shows us the same side. It has a bulge in the center of that side that faces us; a bulge about two miles high.

In order to tell how fast a planet turns on its axis (without the use of microwaves) astronomers would watch for certain markings on its surface and measure the time it took for those markings to disappear round the other side and come back. Accurate measurements can be made on even distant planets in this way.

The rotation of Mercury was hard to measure in this fashion, though. It is so close to the sun that it is difficult to make out its surface features in the glare.

In 1890, Schiaparelli (the astronomer who had first detected the "canals" on Mars) did follow certain features on Mercury. He found that when Mercury was in a certain position with respect to the sun, he could often make out the same markings in the same position. This would be what was to be expected if Mercury always turned with the same face toward the sun and this would happen if it turned on its axis in the same time that it turned about the sun—eighty-eight days.

Astronomers were quite satisfied with that, for it made sense. The huge sun had slowed the rotation of nearby Mercury, as Earth had slowed the rotation of the moon. And, indeed, the first microwave contact made with Mercury seemed to show that that was so.

However, more and better contacts followed and in 1965, astronomers found themselves faced with surprising data. Careful work on microwave echoes from an observatory in

Puerto Rico showed that Mercury did *not* turn on its axis in eighty-eight days, but in a rather shorter time. Other laboratories pointed their microwaves at Mercury at once and the result was found to be correct. Mercury turns on its axis once in fifty-nine days.

But if that is the case, how could Schiaparelli have thought that the revolution was an eighty-eight-day one? Did he make a mistake in observing the markings?

Perhaps not. A period of fifty-nine days is just two-thirds of the eighty-eight-day swing about the sun. This means that every time Mercury moves about the sun two times, it turns on its axis three times.

Imagine that a certain spot on Mercury's surface faces the sun at a particular time. When Mercury has gone around the sun twice, it has turned on its axis three times and the same spot is again facing the sun.

When Schiaparelli observed markings, he would have seen the same one in the same place every other time Mercury turned about the sun. He didn't see them in between but perhaps he paid little attention to that because Mercury was so close to the sun, one couldn't always be sure what one saw anyway. So he made the easy supposition that the markings were probably there everytime, whether he saw them or not, and that Mercury rotated in eighty-eight days.

But again it was Venus that supplied the still greater surprise. That had happened a year before Mercury's rotation had been given a new look.

In the case of Mercury, astronomers at least thought they knew what the time of rotation was, even though they were wrong. In the case of Venus, no one knew. There were never any markings that could be followed.

That was so frustrating. All the other planets had definite rotation times that could be measured (even though Mercury's was measured wrong). Even distant Pluto, over 150 times as far as Venus, was not mysterious in this respect. Pluto is so distant it can only be seen as a dot of light even in a good telescope and no markings can be made out. However, it seems to grow slightly brighter and dimmer in a regular way. Astronomers have decided that this is the result of some part of it being brighter than the rest for some reason; and it is the bright part showing and vanishing as the planet rotates that makes the flicker. Judging by this, Pluto seems to rotate once every 6.4 days.

Yet Venus had no known period of rotation at all. Most astronomers thought that probably Venus's rotation was slowed by the sun and that it showed only one face to the sun. That would mean it would turn on its axis only once each time it turned about the sun—once in 225 days.

But what would radar say?

Radar had its say in 1964, and the answer was a startling one. Venus rotated not once in 225 days, but once in 243 days, so that it did *not* show only one face to the sun. But what really astonished astronomers was that Venus turned in the wrong direction!

To see what we mean by the wrong direction, imagine that you are viewing the solar system from a point high above the Earth's North Pole. All the planets would be seen to move around the sun in the same direction—counterclockwise; that is, the direction opposite to that in which the hands of a clock move about its face. All the large satellites turn counterclockwise about their planets, too, provided they move about the planet's equator. (Neptune's large satellite does not move about its equator and it is exceptional.)

The sun and the planets also rotate about their own axes in counterclockwise fashion. (Uranus is a partial exception. Its axis tips over so far that it seems to be rolling on its side. Astronomers don't know why.)

All these counterclockwise motions are thought to have arisen at the very beginning of the history of the solar system. The solar system began its life as a huge cloud of gas and dust turning slowly in a counterclockwise direction. That counter-clockwise turning remains to this day in all the motions of the various parts of the solar system.

Yet Venus turns about its axis very slowly in the wrong direction. It turns clockwise. This is not because its axis is tipped, as in the case of Uranus. The axis of Venus is almost perfectly upright. . . . Astronomers can't explain this wrong-way motion.

There is an even greater mystery involved, for the period of rotation seems to be tied to Earth. Every once in a while, Earth and Venus reach positions in their orbits which place them as close together as they ever get. Venus manages to turn just four times in that period.

This means that every time Venus comes as close as possible to the Earth, it shows the same face to the Earth. We can't see this, because we can't see through the clouds, but it seems to be so.

But why is it so? Can Earth's gravitational pull have slowed the rotation of Venus and made it show the same face to us at every close approach? How could that be since Earth's gravitational pull is so much less than the sun's. Why would Venus respond to Earth instead of to the sun?

Astronomers don't know. . . . At least, not yet.

So far I have talked about microwaves being sent out from Earth to various bodies in the solar system. How about micro-waves sent out from the various bodies to the Earth?

The sun sends out microwaves, of course. That has been known since 1942. But then every body in the solar system ought to be producing them too.

Every body contains a certain amount of heat and that means it produces a certain amount of radiation. The greater the temperature of the body, the greater the energy of the radiation it produces and, on the average, the shorter the waves making up that radiation.

If a body has a temperature of about 1000° F. or more, it sends out radiation that is so energetic and short wave that some of it appears in the visible light region. The body is "red hot," for it glows a deep red. As the temperature gets still higher, the light grows brighter and shorter in waves. The sun's surface is at 10,000° F. and it radiates brightly all the colors. It even radiates ultraviolet light, which is invisible, but which has more energy and shorter waves than ordinary light.

An object that has a temperature of less than 1000° F. doesn't radiate visible light, but it does radiate all the wavelengths longer than visible light. It radiates infrared light, for instance, which has less energy and longer waves than visible light. We can't see infrared but we can absorb it and feel it as heat. We can feel the heat of a hot iron from a small distance even though it isn't hot enough to glow.

These too-cool-to-glow bodies all radiate microwaves as well and even longer radio waves. Such waves are so long and have so little energy that even the coldest bodies can radiate them. They have so little energy that we can't feel them in any way, but we have instruments that can detect them.

Every body in the solar system radiates a certain quantity of long-wave radiation. The exact quantity and the exact length of the waves depend on the temperature of the body.

By studying the microwaves sent out by the moon or by a planet, we can therefore determine the temperature of the body. The first determination of this sort came in 1946 when two American astronomers, Robert Henry Dicke and R. Beringer, picked up radio waves sent out by the moon.

Promptly, this produced a puzzle. By studying the moon's infrared radiation, it had seemed that the temperature varied a great deal because there was no atmosphere on the moon to hold and spread the heat. At the height of the moon's day, the temperature reached 250° F. in some places, and this is well above the boiling point of water. At the close of the moon's long night, the temperature had dropped to 280° below 0° F. (which we can write as −280° F.).

The microwaves sent out by the moon, however, seemed to show much smaller variations in temperature.

Astronomers decided that the infrared radiation comes from the very surface of the moon, while the radio waves come from some distance below the surface.

As the sun glares down on the moon, the surface heats up. The heat can't penetrate far beneath the moon's surface, however, and the lower layers remain cool. Then, in the moon's night time, the surface layer loses heat but the deeper layers don't.

It may be that about a yard below the surface of the moon, the temperature remains about −40° F. day and night.

Naturally, astronomers went on to try to detect microwave radiation from other planets to see what that would tell them about the temperature of the planets. They could compare that with what they knew the temperature of the planet ought to be considering its distance from the sun.

They expected no surprises, but they got a big one from the very planet that has been turning everything upside down in the 1960s—Venus.

Earlier measurements of infrared radiation from Venus had showed the temperature to be −40° F. This may seem too cold for a planet that is closer to the sun than Earth is. Infrared radiation, however, reaches us from above the cloud layer of Venus. Naturally, that part of the atmosphere of Venus would be cold. It is cold on Earth, too; that is why high mountains have snow on them all year round even when they are located on Earth's equator.

Microwaves are another thing altogether. They can penetrate the cloud layer on Venus easily. Therefore if the solid surface of the planet gives off microwaves, those would go through the cloud layer and reach us. (Infrared radiation wouldn't.) The microwaves would give us the temperature of the solid surface of the planet.

In May of 1956, microwave emission from Venus was finally detected by C. H. Mayer at the Naval Research Laboratories in Washington. Surprisingly, the flood of microwaves was much greater than had been expected. They showed that the surface of Venus must be at a temperature of 600° F. and later measurements backed that up.

Astronomers expected Venus to be a warm world and, because of its thick clouds, sometimes visualized it as covered with a warm ocean. But now it seemed there was no ocean at all, for the planet was far hotter than the boiling point of water.

Any water on Venus would have to be in the form of steam and that might be why the cloud layer on the planet is so thick and permanent. (On the other hand, some astronomers believe that Venus has no water at all and that the clouds are something else.)

But why should Venus be so hot? One explanation involves its atmosphere.

When visible light strikes a planet it passes through the atmosphere and strikes the surface of the planet. The atmosphere doesn't interfere much with such visible light. Even clouds only stop part of the light.

The light that is absorbed by the planet's surface heats it up a little. The surface then gives off radiation of its own that is less energetic than visible light (after all, the planet's surface isn't as hot as the sun). Much of the light radiated by the planet's surface is infrared radiation.

This infrared ought to pass through the atmosphere and vanish into space and the planet, then, with light coming in and infrared going out, would be at a certain temperature.

But there are some gases which are transparent to visible light but not to infrared radiation. One of these is carbon dioxide. Earth's atmosphere has only three-hundredths of 1 percent carbon dioxide but even that small quantity is enough to make it difficult for infrared to get through the atmosphere. The infrared leaks out so slowly that a considerable quantity accumulates and heats up the air and surface of the planet. The temperature of the Earth is higher than it would otherwise be, thanks to the small quantity of carbon dioxide in the atmosphere. (Water vapor also has this effect.)

The same thing happens in a greenhouse. The glass of the greenhouse lets sunlight in but doesn't let infrared radiation out. For that reason, the temperature inside the greenhouse stays warm on sunny days even in cold weather. The action of carbon dioxide and water vapor is therefore referred to as the "greenhouse effect."

The atmosphere of Venus is far richer in carbon dioxide than our own atmosphere. Not only does Venus get more heat from the sun than we do because it is closer to the sun, but the heat is trapped to a much greater extent. This is the most popular explanation for the unusually high temperature of Venus.

It is possible, to be sure, that some microwaves sent out by a planet may not be produced just by its heat. There may be other causes.

This came up as a strong possibility in 1955. In that year, two astronomers, Kenneth Linn Franklin and Bernard F. Burke, at the Carnegie Institution in Washington, were measuring radio waves from the heavens. They received strange interference at one point and wondered what it might be. It could just be static; perhaps some faulty electrical device was sparking somewhere in the vicinity.

However, they kept getting the interference night after night and it seemed to be coming from some particular place in the heavens; some place that was moving from night to night in a particular way. They studied the sky to see if something were in that place that might be moving in just that way, and they found the planet Jupiter in that place and moving in that way.

There was no mistake. Jupiter was sending out strong bursts of microwaves. Going back through the records, they found that strong bursts had been reported from the direction of Jupiter in 1950 and 1951, but no one had followed it up.

When a planet sends out radiation, it sends it out over a broad band of different wavelengths. In receiving the microwaves from Jupiter, then, one could study first one part of the band and then another.

Astronomers could, for instance, study those microwaves that were one or two inches long. When this was done, it was found that the quantity of microwaves received was about what one would expect of a body at a temperature of, say −200° F.

This was the temperature of Jupiter judging from infrared radiation, and about the temperature one would expect for a planet as far from the sun as Jupiter was.

So far, so good, but what about the microwaves with longer wavelengths. There the quantity rose unexpectedly. An object with a temperature of −200° F. couldn't possibly radiate as much long-wave microwaves as Jupiter did, if temperature were the only cause of the radiation.

Jupiter's radiation of four-inch microwaves was what would be expected of a body at a temperature of 700° F. or so. Its radiation of twelve-inch microwaves would have required a temperature of nearly 10,000° F., the temperature of the sun's surface. The radiation of twenty-seven-inch microwaves would have required 90,000° F., hotter than the surface of the hottest stars we can see.

This is quite impossible. Jupiter can't be that hot. It must be sending out long microwaves for other reasons.

One possible cause is related to the fact that Jupiter behaves like a strong magnet. Our own Earth behaves like a magnet, which is why the compass needle always points north, but Jupiter is apparently a much stronger one.

Electrons and other particles streaming out of the sun are trapped in Jupiter's magnetic field and are made to move in rapid spirals high above Jupiter's surface. Such spiraling particles would send out floods of microwaves.

In some wavelengths, though, the microwaves come off in unsteady bursts. Are they produced by gigantic thunderstorms in Jupiter's vast atmosphere, which is much thicker, deeper, and larger than ours? Are there lightning bolts a billion times as strong as those we witness on our own planet, each sending out a crackle of microwaves?

Then, too, as Jupiter rotates about its axis, the quantity of microwaves rises and falls regularly. There seem to be certain places on the planet that are particularly rich sources. What these might be nobody yet knows.

These bursts of microwaves also seem to be stronger than usual whenever Jupiter's innermost large satellite, Io, is in particular positions in its orbit around Jupiter. Why that should be no one knows.

Someday we will find answers and when we do, then through microwaves we will find out more about Jupiter than would have seemed possible just a couple of decades ago.

But all that followed from Jansky's discovery of radio waves from the sky does not exhaust the new studies of the solar system.

Even more dramatic is the other breakthrough I mentioned —the flight of the rocket in 1926. This I will now turn to in the book's last chapter.

As long as we can investigate the planets only from the surface of the Earth, we are limited in what we can find out. No matter how we analyze the light and the radio waves that reach us, there must be so much we miss.

If only we could get closer. If only we could get away from our Earth-prison.

Actually, such a dream doesn't date only from the time of modern astronomy. Men have always longed to free themselves from being bound to the Earth's surface. This is not just to get a better view of the heavens; it is to gain freedom. Surely almost every child at one time or another, watching a bird fly, has wished that he, too, had wings and could swoop through the air.

A famous Greek myth tells of a man who flew. The man was Daedalus, a clever inventor of legend, who was imprisoned on a small island near Crete. He had no boat, so in order to escape from the island he fashioned wings.

He constructed a light framework and stuck feathers to it with wax. By flapping these wings, he could rise in the air and fly. He made another pair for his son, Icarus, and together they flew away.

Daedalus escaped to Sicily. Icarus, however, in the joy of

flying, soared too high and the heat of the sun melted the wax that held the feathers of his wings. He fell to his death.

Of course, wings alone, no matter how feathered and bird-like, can't make you fly. What counts are the muscles that flap them fast enough and maneuver them properly, so as to use the air as a cushion. Human muscles are simply not strong enough to raise the weight of the human body into the air simply by flapping wings.

When man finally did lift off the surface of the Earth, it was not by flapping but by floating. In 1783, two French brothers, Joseph Michel Montgolfier and Jacques Etienne Montgolfier, filled a large linen bag with hot air. Hot air is lighter than the same quantity of cold air (that is, hot air is less dense), so it floats on cold air as wood floats on water. The hot air rose, carrying the bag with it, and drifted for a mile and a half.

Soon larger bags were filled with hydrogen, which is far less dense than hot air. Such bags, or "balloons" could not only lift themselves, but also gondolas carrying human beings.

There was a ballooning craze in the first part of the nineteenth century. For the first time men rose miles high into the air.

Of course, such balloons were at the mercy of the wind. To make it possible for a balloon to go in some particular direction, even against the wind, a motor and a propeller would have to be placed on board. This was first done successfully by a German inventor, Count Ferdinand von Zeppelin, in 1900.

Such "dirigible balloons" eventually carried hundreds of people over wide oceans, but they were terribly fragile. Storms destroyed them. The future of air travel lay elsewhere.

After all must things be lighter than air to be lifted by it? Leaves and pieces of paper are denser than air; if still, they will not float. A brisk wind will, however, set them whirling through the air. If a heavier-than-air object has flat surfaces and if it moves fast enough, those flat surfaces will ride the air and lift the object high.

Toward the end of the nineteenth century there was a glider craze. Light objects, with broad, flat wings, could ride the wind like kites and could carry men with them.

But gliders, like the original balloons, were at the mercy of the wind. Could one place an engine upon them? In 1903, the American brothers, Wilbur Wright and Orville Wright, placed a motor and propeller on a glider of their own design. The propeller pulled the glider through the air quickly enough to raise it into the air and allow it to fly without wind or even against wind. That first power-glider remained in flight for almost a minute.

Thus, the third year of the twentieth century saw the construction of the first "heavier-than-air" flying machine; or, as we call it now, "airplane."

Airplanes have improved and developed until now they are capable of carrying a hundred or more people in luxurious surroundings for thousands of miles at speeds of many hundreds of miles an hour.

Balloons and airplanes both float on air. The difference is that balloons will float even if motionless, while airplanes must travel with great speed in order to ride on moving currents of air.

Neither balloons nor airplanes could rise off the ground if there were no air.

The air gets thinner as one moves higher above the surface of the Earth. Eventually, it gets so thin that neither balloons nor planes will get enough support to move higher. Twenty miles above the Earth's surface represents a reasonable limit.

Even twenty miles rise can be very useful to astronomers. At that height, something like 99 percent of the atmosphere is below the balloon or plane. The trace of air left above can scarcely obscure the heavens in any way, and this is important.

For instance, to reach us here at the low-lying surface of the Earth, the sun's radiation must travel through the twenty miles of thick atmosphere that would lie under a high-flying balloon. The visible light reaches us scarcely diminished, but ultraviolet light and infrared light are mostly absorbed and can't be studied. If sunlight were observed from a height of twenty miles, the ultraviolet and infrared could be studied as carefully as we have studied visible light in the past.

For this reason, photographs have been made of the sun from the gondolas of large balloons, and the sunlight has been carefully analyzed from that height.

As another example, the light reflected to us by Venus shows certain regions of absorption which indicate that light has passed through layers of water vapor molecules on its way to our eyes. Does that mean there is water vapor in Venus's atmosphere and that its clouds are made up of water droplets or ice particles?

Or is it just the water vapor in our own atmosphere?

If the light from Venus were studied from a high balloon, there would be no problem. The balloon would be above the water vapor content of Earth's atmosphere. Any sign of water vapor in the light absorption would have to be caused by water in Venus's atmosphere.

In 1959, light from Venus was studied by an American astronomer, John Strong, from a high-flying balloon. He did indeed detect small quantities of water vapor but, unfortunately, that did not end the problem. Similar studies in high-flying airplanes in 1967 have failed to detect water, so there is still a dispute as to whether Venus's atmosphere contains water vapor or not.

But planes and balloons don't represent complete freedom. They lift man from the surface of the Earth but not more than twenty miles high. Man is still a prisoner of the atmosphere.

Is there any way of rising beyond the atmosphere? There

might be if one weren't forced to depend on floating. There must be some way of lifting an object that could work in a vacuum as well as in air.

One way would be to shoot an object upward out of a giant cannon. Cannonballs may be made to go high in the air this way. The faster they are sent shooting out of the muzzle, the higher they go.

As they go higher and higher, Earth's gravitational force grows slightly weaker so that they go a little higher than one might expect. If they are sent up fast enough, by the time they lose half their speed they are up where Earth's gravity is only half its strength. Though the objects continue to lose speed, so does Earth's gravity continue to lose strength. If the cannonball goes fast enough, Earth's gravity can never bring it to a halt, let alone cause it to start falling back to Earth.

An object which is shot upward at such a velocity that it never returns is said to have been fired at "escape velocity." For Earth, escape velocity is 7 miles per second, or 25,200 miles an hour. If a large hollow object with people inside could be fired upward at 7 miles per second (or more), it would rise and rise and continue to rise. If it were aimed correctly, it would rise to the moon.

In 1865, the French science fiction writer Jules Verne wrote *From the Earth to the Moon,* a novel describing how a group of men are hurled to the moon in this fashion.

Unfortunately, the method, while correct in theory, is not practical. Not only would it require an enormous cannon that is not likely ever to be built, but if a spaceship were fired out of a cannon in this way, the sudden increase of speed (or "acceleration") would kill every person on board in a moment.

Another method, though, is to make use of the "law of action and reaction," which was first announced by Isaac Newton in 1687. This law explains that if a portion of a body is thrown off in one direction, the rest of the body must move in the opposite direction.

Imagine yourself sitting on a smooth aluminum platter resting on a sheet of smooth ice. With you are a bunch of heavy steel balls. If you threw one of the balls away with all your might, the platter carrying you and the rest of the balls would start sliding in the opposite direction. Throw a second ball after the first and the platter will move more quickly. Keep it up, and if you have enough balls you will end by skimming along the ice quite rapidly.

In 1891, an eccentric German inventor, Hermann Ganswindt, suggested a trip beyond the atmosphere by using this method. (He was the first man to try to design a spaceship along scientific principles.) Instead of throwing steel balls by hand, he imagined a ship that would fire them out to the rear by dynamite explosions.

If enough steel balls were hurled backward with enough speed and in sufficient quantity, the ship would reach escape velocity. It would then travel away from the Earth indefinitely. The important difference between this and a cannon is that the speed would be built up slowly over a long period in Ganswindt's ship, where it would build up all at once before the ship left the muzzle in Verne's cannon. Acceleration would not be murderous in Ganswindt's ship.

But why fire out heavy objects? If a ship fired out a jet of gas from the rear, that could do the job, too, provided the gas were fired out quickly enough.

The advantage of gas over solids is that gas can be made to shoot out in a continuous stream. The ship would gain speed smoothly instead of in a series of jerks and it would do so more efficiently.

We can actually watch a gas jet do the work of moving an object. Suppose you fill a toy balloon with air, hold it up and let the air escape. The air, rushing out in one direction, will cause the balloon to move in the other.

For such action and reaction to take place, air does not have to surround the moving object. In fact, air gets in the way. When escaping air moves a balloon, the balloon's motion is slowed by the resistance of the air all about it. The balloon is pushed this way and that by air currents. Action and reaction would work best in a vacuum where nothing would interfere with motion.

Actually, the spherical shape of a balloon is bad for rapid motion. To allow for rapid motion through air with least interference, you need an object that is narrow and streamlined. Then, too, you want as much gas in it as possible so that it will come out with great speed and in large quantities. One way of packing an object with much gas is to pack it with a solid that can be easily and quickly turned into a gas.

Suppose you take a narrow cylinder, coming to a pointed end on one side and open at the other. Fill it with gunpowder, close the open end lightly, and push a fuse through into the gunpowder. Once the fuse is lit, the gunpowder will quickly catch fire and form large quantities of gas. A hot jet of these gases will push out this "rocket," which will then move rapidly in the opposite direction. Small rockets shot into the air in this way on the Fourth of July can be very impressive.

Large rockets of this same sort might easily be used as a war weapon. By sending burning rockets into a city, buildings could be set afire, munitions could be set to exploding, and people could be panicked. For a while in the nineteenth century such rockets were indeed used in warfare. They were used in the War of 1812 between the United States and Great Britain. *The Star-Spangled Banner,* our national anthem, written during that war, speaks of "the rockets' red glare."

Rockets faded out as a war weapon because cannonballs could be fired more accurately from cannon and would do more damage.

However, rockets remain more practical for reaching great heights than cannon. A cannon must fire off all its gunpowder before the cannonball comes out of the muzzle. After that the cannonball can only slow down. A rocket rises up while the gunpowder is still burning, and it carries the gunpowder up- ward along with itself. As it rises, it therefore goes faster and faster as more and more of the gunpowder burns.

In order for the ordinary rocket to work, however, it must be surrounded by air while the gunpowder is burning, for the gunpowder won't burn in the absence of air. This means that such a rocket can accelerate only inside the atmosphere.

Acceleration inside the atmosphere is important for many purposes, to be sure. The rocket principle can be applied to airplanes very neatly.

At first, airplanes were sped through the air by means of a propeller. The propeller was the weak point of the plane. Its tips had to move through the air much more quickly than the plane itself did. There was a limit to how quickly propellers could be whirled and that helped set a limit to how quickly planes could fly.

Suppose, though, that you fed gasoline into a rocket ar- rangement, had it burn, and sent the gases out through the rear. The plane would then be driven forward without a pro- peller. At high speeds, such a "jet plane" is much more effi- cient than a propeller plane. Indeed, a jet plane can easily reach speeds a propeller plane could never achieve.

The jet plane was developed during World War II as a war weapon. In 1952, it made its first appearance in commer- cial aviation and travel by jet is now very common. Jet planes can easily go faster than the speed of sound, which is 750 miles an hour, or 0.2 miles a second.

If a jet plane built up enough speed and reached escape velocity, it could leave the atmosphere altogether and enter space. It would need no further jet blasts to continue onward indefinitely.

This is not practical, though. The jet that drives the plane is kept going by fuel burning in air drawn in from the sur- rounding atmosphere. This means that the jet only works where the atmosphere is fairly dense. All the acceleration must take place in this dense atmosphere, where air resistance is so high it would waste fuel and would heat up the ship dangerously.

It would be much better if the jet plane could reach the upper atmosphere at low speeds, avoiding too much resistance and heating. Then up there, where the atmosphere is too thin to be any trouble, the real job of acceleration could take place. Unfortunately, up there the atmosphere is too thin to keep the gasoline burning.

A spaceship must, therefore, carry its own supply of air (or, better, oxygen) along with the fuel. Then, once the spaceship got into the upper atmosphere, it could mix its stored fuel with its stored oxygen, burn the mixture, and accelerate to escape velocity without trouble.

A self-educated Russian schoolteacher, Konstantin Eduardovich Tsiolkovsky, was the first to make this clear. In 1898, he wrote a long article in which he described a spaceship that would be powered by a rocket exhaust. It was published, finally, in 1903, the same year in which the airplane was invented. It was the first description of the kind of spaceship that eventually came into use.

The real breakthrough, however, came in the United States, through the work of an American rocket engineer, Robert Hutchings Goddard.

As a boy, he was fascinated by science fiction. In 1899, he read *War of the Worlds* by Herbert George Wells, a thrilling adventure in which Martians invade Earth and almost conquer it. With that began Goddard's lifelong dream of penetrating outer space. By 1901, he was writing essays on the possibility of space travel.

Both Goddard and Tsiolkovsky saw that the older rockets were unsuitable. When gunpowder was used, its burning could not easily be controlled and it did not produce a fast enough exhaust anyway. Both men felt that what was really needed was a liquid fuel. This could be pumped into a chamber where it could be burned. The pumping could be started or stopped, made to go fast or slow. The exhaust could thus be controlled.

Tsiolkovsky was content merely to theorize, but Goddard went further. He began to design actual rocket engines. In 1914, he obtained two patents for inventions to be used in such engines. In 1919, he finally published a small book (only sixty-nine pages) on the subject.

Now he was ready to build small rocket engines and see how they worked. In 1923, he tested an engine in which a stored supply of gasoline and a stored supply of liquid oxygen were contained. The two liquids were pumped into the burning chamber where they were mixed and ignited. The engine worked well and the next step, Goddard decided, was to send a liquid-fuel rocket upward.

He was teaching at Clark University in Worcester at this time, and he performed his experiments on an aunt's farm in Auburn, Massachusetts.

There, on March 16, 1926, he made ready to fire his rocket. His wife took a picture of him standing next to it. It was a cold day and there was snow on the ground. Goddard, wearing overcoat and boots, was standing next to what seemed a child's jungle gym. At the top of the structure was a small rocket, four feet long and six inches thick.

There were no reporters present and no one was interested in what he was doing. That was too bad, for what was about to happen was one of the news stories of the century, if only the world had known. The first liquid-fuel rocket was about to rise into the air.

Goddard ignited it and the rocket rose 184 feet into the air, reaching a speed of 60 miles an hour. This wasn't much, but it showed that Goddard's rocket engine worked. It was only necessary to build improved rockets on a larger scale.

Goddard managed to get a few thousand dollars from the

Smithsonian Institution and continued his work. In July 1929, he sent up a larger rocket, which went faster and higher than the first. More important, it carried a barometer and a thermometer, along with a small camera to photograph their readings. This was the first instrument-carrying rocket.

Unfortunately, Goddard now ran into trouble. News had leaked out that he was trying to reach the moon and many people began to laugh at him. *The New York Times* printed an editorial telling him his science was all wrong. (Actually, the editorial writer was quite foolish, for he didn't even understand the law of action and reaction, thinking that air was necessary for its working—yet he dared lecture an expert like Goddard.)

When one of Goddard's rockets made a loud noise while being launched, policemen and firemen were called and he was ordered to conduct no more rocket experiments in Massachusetts.

But Charles Augustus Lindbergh, the famous aviator, had heard of Goddard's experiments and he used his influence to get the rocket engineer some financial help. Goddard built a new rocket-launching site in New Mexico, where he could experiment without disturbing anybody.

Here he built larger rockets and developed many of the ideas now used in all rockets. He showed how to build a combustion chamber of the proper shape and how to keep its walls cool. He showed how the rocket could be steered and how it could be kept on a straight course.

He also worked out and patented the notion of multi-stage rockets. A two-stage rocket, for instance, consists of a small rocket built on a large one. The large one burns its fuel and carries itself and the small rocket up into the upper atmosphere. Then the large rocket, empty of fuel, breaks loose and drops away, while the small rocket goes into action.

High up where the air is too thin to interfere, the small rocket's fuel blasts off. It is already moving upward at considerable speed thanks to the action of the large rocket, and now its own engine makes it go higher still.

The small rocket moves a lot higher and faster than the whole rocket would have moved if it were all one piece.

In the early 1930s, Goddard finally fired rockets that reached speeds faster than sound and rose a mile and a half into the air. The American government was never really interested in this work while Goddard was alive, but years after his death, it had to pay a million dollars for the use of two hundred of his patents. Work on rockets would have come to a dead halt otherwise.

Interest in rocket experiments was particularly great in Germany. In 1923, a book on space travel was published in that country by Hermann Oberth, who was born in a region that is now part of Rumania. By 1927, a "Society for Space Travel" had been founded in Germany. Its young and enthusiastic members began to plan rocket experiments. Similar societies were formed in other countries but the German society was by far the most successful.

Among the members of the German society were two young men, Willy Ley and Wernher von Braun, each destined for great fame. They threw themselves into rocket-building and in the next couple of years some eighty-five rockets were fired. One reached an altitude of nearly a mile.

Goddard was doing even better, but he was a lone wolf, ignored by the United States. The German rocket engineers were soon receiving government support. When Adolf Hitler came to power in Germany in 1933, he began to think of the new rockets as a possible war weapon.

In 1936, a secret experimental station was built at Peenemunde, on the Baltic seacoast of Germany. There, by 1938, rockets capable of flying eleven miles were built. Such rockets might be expensive just at first, but they flew by themselves and required no human pilots. They could be aimed quite accurately and they went so quickly they couldn't even be detected, let alone stopped.

The first rocket-driven "missile" was fired in 1942 and by 1944, Wernher von Braun's group put these missiles into action. They were the famous V-2 rockets. (The V stood for *vergeltung,* meaning "vengeance.")

In all, 4,300 V-2 rockets were fired during World War II and of these, 1,230 hit London. Von Braun's missiles killed 2,511 Englishmen and seriously wounded 5,869 others. Luckily for the world, the V-2 came too late. Hitler had lost the war and the V-2 couldn't reverse that decision.

Goddard lived just long enough to see this awful triumph of the rocket. He died on August 10, 1945.

One thing the V-2 rocket did was to rouse the interest of Germany's adversaries, the United States and the Soviet Union. Immediately after the war, both made efforts to capture Germany's rocket experts. The United States got most of them, including Wernher von Braun. (Willy Ley had left Germany for the United States long before—as soon as Hitler came to power.)

Both nations then worked hard to build missiles. By the 1950s the old V-2 was a piddling affair compared to the monsters that were coming into existence. Both the Soviet Union and the United States developed "Inter-Continental Ballistic Missiles" (ICBMs). These could travel for thousands of miles and land accurately on target.

Both nations could strike any place on Earth, now, with missiles based on their own territory. These missiles could carry hydrogen bombs. A new world war would be more terrible than had ever been imagined. In the space of half an hour, hundreds of millions of people could die, and civilization might be destroyed.

But rockets were not used only for war weapons. Some were sent up into the heavens in order that new knowledge might be brought back. Soon after the war, captured V-2 missiles were used by the United States to carry instruments into the upper atmosphere. One reached a height of 114 miles, five times as high as any plane or balloon could reach.

In 1949, the United States put a small American rocket on top of a V-2. When the V-2 had reached its maximum height, the small rocket took off and reached a height of 240 miles.

Another way of accomplishing the same purpose was to send a balloon as high into the atmosphere as possible and then to launch a small rocket from it. The air would be too thin to interfere and such a "rockoon" combination could reach great heights with very little expense. A leader in this work was the American physicist James Alfred Van Allen.

Such high-flying rockets brought back useful information about the nature of the upper atmosphere. They described the temperature, density, winds, gases, and ions of the upper atmosphere and recorded how all of these changed from time to time.

But such rockets only stayed in the upper air a short period of time and could only gather information concerning the portion immediately about it. What was wanted was a rocket that could stay up for a long time.

Suppose a rocket were sent up at a velocity less than escape, and was steered so as to travel parallel to the surface of the Earth. Since it could be traveling at less than escape velocity, it would fall toward the Earth. The surface of the Earth, however, is curved. The surface curves away from the rocket as the rocket falls while moving forward.

If the speed of the rocket is just right, then it will travel so far parallel to the Earth's surface while it is falling a mile that the Earth's surface will have curved away one mile. In that case the rocket will never actually fall to Earth, but will circle it forever. The rocket will be "in orbit" about the Earth; it will become a "man-made satellite" of our planet.

If the speed and direction of the rocket is *just* right, it will go about the Earth in a perfect circle. Otherwise it will circle the Earth in an ellipse. This ellipse can be quite oval, sort of long and flattened. The satellite could come quite close to the surface of the Earth on one side of its orbit and be quite far away at the other.

Although, in theory, such a satellite should stay in space forever, part or all of its orbit might be within 100 or 150 miles of the Earth's surface. In that case, the very thin air of the upper atmosphere will produce enough resistance to consume the satellite's energy of motion very slowly. The satellite will spiral lower and lower and eventually penetrate the thick atmosphere and burn up.

Rocket experts began thinking of possible satellites in connection with a huge international study of our planet planned for 1957 and 1958 (the "International Geophysical Year" or IGY). Perhaps the launching of a satellite could be made part of the IGY. On July 29, 1955, the American government officially announced the attempt would be made.

The Soviet Union then announced that it would also make such an attempt, but most Americans paid no attention. Those that did thought the Soviets were just playing "copy-cat" and that only the United States had the ability to perform such a difficult rocket feat.

The Soviet Union therefore surprised the whole world (and particularly the United States) when, on October 4, 1957, they launched the first successful satellite. This was meant to celebrate the hundredth anniversary of the birth of Tsiolkovsky (which had taken place on September 17). They called it "Sputnik," meaning "satellite," a name that Tsiolkovsky himself had used to describe such man-made objects in orbit.

The United States was soon launching satellites of its own. On January 31, 1958, the first successful American satellite, Explorer I, was launched. In the years that followed, hundreds of satellites were launched by each nation.

These satellites turned out to have a great many practical

uses. For instance, some were designed to take many thousands of photographs of the Earth. Such photographs would show the cloud pattern over large areas. Scientists would learn more about the way in which air circulated and clouds formed. They could watch the birth and development of hurricanes. They could predict weather more accurately.

The first satellite intended for such a weather-watch was launched on April 1, 1960. It was called TIROS (standing for "Television and Infra-Red Observation Satellite) and it proved to be a great success. Soon, the sight of the Earth as seen from hundreds of miles in the air grew to be common.

Eight such satellites were launched altogether and then a more advanced type of satellite, "Nimbus," was launched on August 28, 1964.

Satellites can also be used for communications. Ordinary radio waves bounce off the charged particles in the ionosphere. That makes it possible to send radio messages around the world. Short radio waves, like those used in television, go right through the ionosphere. However, if they could be made to strike a satellite outside the Earth's atmosphere, they could be reflected back to another part of the Earth.

This was first pointed out in 1945 by Arthur C. Clarke, a young Englishman who was to become one of the best science fiction writers in the world. Another science fiction enthusiast, the American engineer John Robinson Pierce, who worked at the Bell Telephone Laboratories, endeavored to bring this idea to reality.

On August 12, 1960, Echo I, made possible by work at Bell Telephone, was launched. It carried a collapsed plastic balloon which was inflated, once it was in space, into a huge sphere that was as tall as a ten-story building. Radio waves striking it were reflected, and messages could be sent from continent to continent in this way.

Messages reflected from Echo I were very weak by the time they were received, of course. On July 10, 1962, Telstar I was launched. It did more than receive messages; it amplified them once received and made them stronger. Then it sent the strengthened signals back to Earth. This meant that American television sets could now easily receive pictures live from Europe and vice versa.

These early "communications satellites" were close to the Earth and traveled rapidly around it. They could only be used to transmit messages across the Atlantic when they happened to be in the right spot above the Atlantic.

If a satellite is sent higher and higher, it takes longer and longer to travel about the Earth. If it is about 22,300 miles above the Earth's surface, it takes twenty-four hours to circle the Earth, or just the time it takes the planet to turn on its axis. The satellite moves in time with the planet and is always over a particular spot on the surface. Clarke had suggested satellites of this kind.

This was achieved with full success on August 19, 1964, when Syncom III was launched. It was placed over the Pacific Ocean just in time to make it possible to broadcast the Olympic Games, live, from Tokyo to the United States.

Satellites can also be used to help determine the shape of the Earth. The Earth is not a perfect sphere. Because it turns, a centrifugal effect tends to lift its matter upward against gravity. (If you attach a heavy object firmly to a cord and whirl it rapidly round your head, you will feel it pull away from your hand.)

The Earth turns most rapidly in the equatorial regions. Its matter lifts up highest there. The Earth has an "equatorial bulge," therefore, that is thirteen miles high at the equator.

On March 17, 1958, Vanguard I was launched. It was a tiny thing, only the second satellite the United States had placed in orbit, and all it carried was a small radio sending out a steady signal. Its motion could be followed by that signal, and that was sufficient to be useful.

Vanguard I had an orbit that was at an angle to the equator.

In part of its orbit it was north of the equatorial bulge and in the other part it was south. The bulge had a special gravitational effect on the tiny satellite and altered its orbit in a way that scientists could easily calculate.

Scientists expected that the bulge would have the same effect on the satellite whether it was to the north or the south. That turned out not to be so. The part of the bulge south of the equator turned out to be a little higher than the part north.

Indeed, by studying the orbit of Vanguard I and later satellites very carefully, scientists could determine all kinds of bulges and hollows in the Earth's surface, even though these were only a few dozen feet high or low.

By knowing the Earth's shape more exactly than ever before, it became possible to make maps with greater accuracy. It turned out that some islands were a mile or more away from where the old maps had showed them to be. For the first time, the distance between London and New York could be worked out to within a few feet.

What's more, ships could locate their own positions on the ocean with new accuracy, by observing satellites.

Nor was it only knowledge of the Earth itself that was the product of satellite work. Those portions of space through which the satellites traveled could be studied in detail for the first time. Ordinary telescopes could see nothing there, but did that mean that nothing was really there? What about cosmic ray particles?

Explorer I, America's first satellite, carried special devices to record cosmic ray and other electrically charged particles. Its orbit was elliptical enough to bring it as close to 217 miles to Earth's surface in one part of its orbit and take it out to 1,155 miles in the opposite part. It could record charged particles at all heights between.

Up to a height of 500 miles, the number of particles recorded per minute was about as expected, and increased slowly as the height increased. Above 500 miles, however, the number of detected particles dropped suddenly, sometimes all the way to zero.

Scientists wondered if it might not be that the instrument was out of order. But then a later satellite sent back the same kind of records.

James A. Van Allen, in charge of these experiments, thought the trouble might be that there were so many charged particles that they were "blinding" the instruments. On July 26, 1958, Explorer IV was launched. Its instruments were designed to handle very high quantities of particles and now things were different.

Around the Earth, there proved to be regions that were enormously rich in charged particles. These were sent out by the sun (the "Solar wind") and were trapped by the Earth's magnetic field. These particle-rich regions were called "Van Allen belts."

The belts came closest to the Earth near the magnetic poles in the polar regions. There the charged particles leaked into the atmosphere and produced the beautiful shifting colors of the aurora (or "Northern Lights").

At first, it was thought these belts were perfectly even, all around the Earth. Further satellite studies showed that the solar wind struck the Van Allen belts and flattened them on the sun-side. The solar wind then veered to either side, circled the Earth and passed on beyond. The Van Allen belts on the night-side of the planet were drawn out almost as though they were a comet tail.

The lopside area inside the solar wind and circling the Earth is now called the "magnetosphere." No one suspected its existence until the age of satellites had opened.

But satellites need not be restricted to the neighborhood of the Earth. If they are made to go at velocities that are a little faster they can reach the moon. They can escape from Earth altogether and take up orbits about the sun as "man-made planets."

The first successful "Lunar probe," that is, the first satellite to pass near the moon, was sent up by the Soviet Union on January 2, 1959. It was "Lunik I." It was the first man-made object to take up an orbit about the sun, and within two months, the United States had duplicated the feat.

On September 12, 1959, the Soviets sent up Lunik II and it was aimed so accurately that it hit the moon. For the first time in history a man-made object rested on the surface of another world.

Then, a month later, the Soviet satellite Lunik III slipped beyond the moon and pointed a television camera at the side we never see from Earth. (The moon always faces the same side toward us.)

Lunik III changed the photographs into radio signals that could be transmitted to Earth and changed back into photographs. They were fuzzy and of poor quality, but they showed something interesting.

The side of the moon we see is covered with craters but there are also large flat "maria" (or "seas") which are dark in color and have hardly any craters. It is the maria that make the dim splotches on the face of the moon that cause some people to imagine they see the "man in the moon" there.

On the other side of the moon, though, as revealed by Lunik III, there are hardly any maria and no sizable ones at all. A number of satellites since Lunik III, both American and Russian, have made similar photographs of far better quality, and this is borne out. There are no maria to speak of on the other side of the moon.

Astronomers don't know why.

Lunar probes also reported on conditions in the neighborhood of the moon. It was found that the moon did not behave like a magnet and did not have any Van Allen belts of its own.

This was not surprising, really. In order for a heavenly object to behave like a magnet and collect belts of charged particles, it should have a core of melted iron and it should turn rapidly. The turning sets up swirls of liquid in the melted iron and these swirls are what cause the planet to act like a magnet.

The moon is too small to have a melted iron core, and even if it had one, it rotated on its axis too slowly (once in twenty-seven days) to set up important swirls.

Such observations could be made in greater detail by satellites sent into the neighborhood of the moon, and then maneuvered (by tiny bursts of rocket fuel set off by radio message from Earth) into orbit about the moon. This is a most delicate feat but by 1966, both the Soviet Union and the United States had worked out their rocket techniques so well that they could do it.

The Soviet Union's "Luna 10" took up an orbit about the moon after having been launched on March 31, 1966. The United States satellite, "Lunar Orbiter 1" was launched on August 10, 1966, and was the first of several like it.

The Lunar Orbiters took pictures of various portions of the moon's surface. Some of them were from an angle so that the rolling hilly nature could be seen clearly. Such photographs looked just like a desolate desert might seem on Earth. It was hard to believe they were taken of another world, a quarter of a million miles out in space.

Even more startling, perhaps, were pictures taken, past the curve of the moon's surface, of the Earth. There was our own planet, seen as a thick "crescent Earth," from a distance of a quarter of a million miles.

From the orbits of the satellites circling the moon, astronomers were able to figure out the exact location of the center of the moon. Combining that with studies of radar echos, as described in the previous chapter, they found they could calculate the diameter of the moon down to a fraction of a mile.

Pictures of the moon from probes and orbiters that flew by and around the body might be startling but they were usually taken from a considerable distance. What about really close photographs?

The United States planned a whole series of probes designed to strike the moon and take photos on their way down. These satellites were called "Rangers." Ranger I through Ranger V were test satellites that were not sent to the moon. Finally, on January 30, 1964, Ranger VI was launched and headed for the moon. The aiming was very good and it hit the moon only twenty miles from target—but the television cameras failed.

A half-year later, on July 28, 1964, Ranger VII was shot into the sky and this time everything worked perfectly. Photographs were taken, right down to the very moment of impact, and the portion of the moon in view of the cameras was seen with greater detail than had ever before been possible.

Some astronomers had thought that the moon might be covered by a thick layer of fine dust, and they searched the Ranger photographs for some sign of that. Most astronomers felt that no dust showed up, but the matter wasn't settled.

What was needed was a "soft landing." Until 1966, all the probes that had reached the moon's surface had made a "hard landing," hitting with such force that they had been destroyed. If a satellite fired rockets downward just before landing, however, its speed of fall would be slowed up and it might then come down gently enough to allow its instruments to keep working. This would be a soft landing.

Both the Soviet Union and the United States tried for a soft landing and both succeeded. On January 31, 1966, the Soviet probe, Luna 9, was launched and succeeded in landing softly on February 3. It took the first pictures of the moon from its surface.

On May 30, 1966, the Americans launched Surveyor I, which landed softly on the Moon by June 2 and which took additional photographs. These and other such successful attempts seem to have made it quite clear by now that the moon's surface is rather like the Earth's. No signs of any dust layer have been detected. One of the later Surveyors even dug up a shovelful of moon soil on signal from Earth and a television camera scanning that soil showed it to be a rather usual soil. Another surveyor carried through a delicate analysis of Lunar soil in 1967 and showed it to resemble earthly basalt.

What about heavenly bodies farther than the moon? The next nearest bodies of importance are Venus and Mars, and both the Soviet Union and the United States have attempted to send out "planetary probes" in the direction of these two bodies.

So far, the Soviet Union has been plagued with bad luck in this respect. One of the "Venus probes," named "Venus 3," actually landed on the planet on March 1, 1966, but the feat was a disappointing one, for the probe's instruments had failed and no information was sent back.

A more successful Venus probe was the American "Mariner II."

It was launched on August 27, 1962, and traveled through space for four months to make its rendezvous with Venus. The probe skimmed by within 21,000 miles of Venus on December 14, 1962. At that time, it was thirty-five million miles from Earth but successfully returned the information it gathered. It was a wonderful example of good aim and clever communications.

Mariner II was able to study the space in the neighborhood of Venus. It found that Venus was not a magnet and did not have any Van Allen belts. To be sure, Venus was large enough (almost as large as the Earth) to have a melted iron core. However, it turned on its axis even more slowly than the moon, so it set up no swirls in that core.

The most exciting thing that Mariner II did was to scan the surface of Venus for microwaves. Astronomers had received microwaves from Venus in such quantity that they had decided the surface of the planet must be exceedingly hot.

This was such a surprising fact, though, that they were eager to have the microwaves studied at close range. Mariner II did this little job and the earlier findings were confirmed. Venus did indeed seem to be very hot.

On October 19, 1967, an even more sophisticated American probe, Mariner 5, flew past Venus. At the same time, a Soviet probe, Venus 4, landed on the planet and this time sent back information. Venus's high temperature was confirmed and its atmosphere, much thicker than Earth's, seemed almost entirely carbon dioxide.

Spectacular rocket successes were also carried through in connection with Mars.

On November 28, 1964, "Mariner IV" was launched in the direction of Mars. Mars is the more distant of the two planets and the journey took eight months. On July 15, 1965, Mariner IV edged past Mars at a distance of little more than 6,000 miles. The information gathered by the probe had to be relayed back to Earth over a distance of nearly 150 million miles.

Mariner IV investigated the space near Mars in a number of ways. It reported on the concentration of dust and particles, the strength of the solar wind, and on the magnetic nature of the planet. It quickly turned out that Mars, like the moon, was too small to have much of a melted iron core. It was no magnet and had no Van Allen belts.

Mariner IV was able to check on the density of the atmosphere of Mars and this turned out to be only one-tenth of what astronomers had thought.

This was important. Astronomers had long suspected there

might possibly be life on Mars. By this, they didn't mean the kind of intelligent, canal-building life that Percival Lowell had speculated about (as described in the previous chapter). Astronomers didn't accept that, but they thought it just barely possible that very simple forms of plant life might exist.

The reason for considering this possibility was that Mars has a climate that does not completely eliminate the chance of life. It is colder than Earth and the air is thinner and there is no oxygen and very little water. Still, some very simple forms of Earth life could be made to live under conditions that were similar to those that astronomers thought existed on Mars. If there were Martian life, it would be especially adapted to Martian conditions, and it would get along even better than Earth life would.

Besides, there actually seemed to be signs of life on Mars.

Mars had ice caps just as the Earth had, though the Martian ice caps were much smaller. Its axis was tipped so that the northern hemisphere had spring and summer when the southern hemisphere had fall and winter, and vice versa, just as was true on Earth.

As seen through the telescope, Mars had reddish areas that might be desert, and dark areas that might, just possibly, be a sign of plant life. When spring came to one of the hemispheres, the ice cap on that side would begin to melt and the dark areas would grow darker and larger, almost as though plant life were flourishing because water from the ice caps was soaking into the soil.

But that notion seemed less likely thanks to the unexpected thinness of the Martian atmosphere. It was only 1/100 as dense as Earth's instead of 1/10 as had been thought, and that seemed to make the possibility of life a poorer one.

Of course, it might have been that the Martian atmosphere was thicker ages ago and that more water had been present then. Life would have started and might then have slowly adapted itself as conditions grew ever harder.

Arguing against this was the most astonishing feat of Mariner IV. These were the photographs it took of Mar's surface and then transmitted to Earth. Mariner II might have taken pictures of Venus but all it would have gotten would have been unbroken, featureless clouds. Mars, however, had very few clouds, if any, and its surface lay exposed.

Twenty-one photographs were taken. They were of poor quality and not at all clear but they showed the Martian surface in far greater detail than it had ever been seen from Earth.

When the pictures were received on Earth, there was instant astonishment. It turned out that the surface of Mars was riddled with craters, just like those on the moon. These were craters that had never been seen through the telescope because Mars was so far away and because its atmosphere, thin as it was, blurred the fine detail on the surface.

But there they were now. More than seventy craters were counted on the various photographs and one of them was seventy-five miles across. Astronomers, such as Fred Whipple of Harvard, and Tombaugh, the discoverer of Pluto, had predicted there might be craters on Mars, but few seemed to take such speculations seriously. Now they had to.

The existence of craters makes it seem that not only is the air thin now, but it may have been very thin through all of Mars's history. There may have been very little water, too. Only in that way could the craters have survived. Otherwise, the action of air and water would have smoothed them down.

The chances for life on Mars looked considerably worse than they had looked before, but not all astronomers were disheartened. It was pointed out that satellites much closer to Earth than Mariner IV had been to Mars could see no signs of life on Earth. A still closer look is required.

A number of projects are being considered whereby a Mars

probe might make a soft landing on Mars. It would carry an instrument that would test for possible life on Mars. A sticky string might be cast out into Martian soil, then pulled back into the craft. Perhaps some Martian bacteria or one-celled plants might stick to the string. If the string were then placed in certain chemicals, the living cells might bring about changes in those chemicals and information about the changes could be transmitted back to Earth.

That, however, is for the future.

More spectacular still than soft landings on the moon and probes passing by Venus and Mars is the notion of sending men into space!

No matter how many instruments we send to the moon and how much information they gather, they could not possibly excite the world as much as would the landing of men upon another world.

But can men survive the rocket takeoff into space? They will have to undergo strong accelerations. They will feel as though they were being pressed down by weights of hundreds of pounds.

Then, once they are in space, with the rocket engines turned off, they will be in "free fall." They will be falling constantly even though they never hit the Earth and they will feel no weight in consequence. They will feel weightless all the time they are in orbit.

What's more, there is the question of radiation out in space. How dangerous are the solar wind and the Van Allen belts?

From the very beginning, the satellite program was geared to such questions both in the Soviet Union and the United States. The second satellite sent up, the Soviet Union's Sputnik II, launched on November 3, 1957, carried a dog. The dog survived the takeoff and the weightlessness and lived until it was painlessly poisoned. There was no way of bringing it back to Earth, however.

Later, as techniques improved, both nations sent all sorts of animals into orbit—mice, dogs, even chimpanzees—and brought them back. They also began to train men for trips into space. In the United States, these men were called "astronauts"; in the Soviet Union, they were called "cosmonauts."

The first step was merely to put the men into orbit about the Earth. In orbit, the men could be brought back after only a few hours in space. They would also stay beneath the possibly dangerous Van Allen belts.

The United States took elaborate precautions to make sure the men would be brought back safely. They set up a worldwide network of observers and planned to have the satellites make landings in the ocean with navy ships standing by.

The Soviet Union worked more secretly and without seeking the cooperation of other nations. This made tracking harder for them. They also planned for the return of the satellite, by parachute, to a land surface, which also made things harder.

Even so, the Soviet Union got men into space first. On April 12, 1961, the Soviet cosmonaut Yuri Gagarin was launched in the spaceship Vostok I. It was shot into orbit, traveled once around the Earth in 108 minutes, and was brought safely back to Earth.

On August 6, 1961, less than four months later, the feat was repeated. Another Soviet cosmonaut, Gherman Titov, was launched in Vostok II. He remained in space through seventeen orbits, which kept him weightless for over twenty-five hours before being returned to Earth.

Then, on February 20, 1962, the United States put its first man into orbit. This was John Herschel Glenn, Jr., who made three orbits in just under five hours and was brought back safely.

In the years that have passed since those first manned launchings, both nations have put more men in orbit for longer and longer periods. The Soviet Union, on June 14,

1963, launched Valery F. Bykovsky, who stayed in space five days, circling the Earth eighty-one times before coming down.

While he was still in orbit, Valentina V. Tereshkova was launched on June 16, 1963. She was the first woman in space. She has since married and had a child, so the experience seems to have done her no harm.

The American-manned space program took up speed as President John Fitzgerald Kennedy called for an American on the moon by 1970. The first few American launchings were in Mercury capsules, little one-man jobs, nine feet high and six feet wide, weighing one and a half tons. In 1965, more ambitious capsules were put in use for the "Gemini" project. This is the Latin word for "twins" and it is used because the new craft was to carry two men.

The Gemini craft was twice as large and twice as heavy as the Mercury. To put a Mercury into orbit required 360,000 pounds of thrust; the Gemini required 530,000 pounds.

On August 21, 1965, a Gemini capsule carrying L. Gordon Cooper and Charles Conrad stayed in orbit for eight days for a new endurance record. The Russians retained another, though, for on October 12, 1964, a Soviet spacecraft was launched with a crew of three. In 1968, a three-man American craft, the Apollo-7 remained in orbit eleven days.

Both the Soviet Union and the United States have, or will soon have, sufficient power to send a ship of the required size to the moon. The United States is experimenting with the Saturn V rocket, which will have a thrust of 7,600,000 pounds. This would be enough to launch a forty-five-ton object into space.

Sheer power, however, is not all that is required. There must be complex maneuvering, as ships move into lunar orbit, and as smaller ships leave larger ones to descend to the moon and then return. It is necessary for astronauts to learn how to rendezvous; that is, to bring one ship into contact with another. It is also necessary for astronauts to learn how to leave the ship, if necessary, and maneuver in space, clad in a spacesuit, powered by a hand-rocket, and linked to the ship by a lifeline.

On March 18, 1965, during the course of a two-man Soviet space flight, the cosmonaut Aleksei A. Leonov stepped out of his capsule and became the first man in history to take a "spacewalk." On June 3, 1965, an American astronaut, Edward H. White, duplicated the feat.

In 1966, the United States was suddenly alone in the field. For some unexplained reason, Soviet manned flights ceased, though they continued to launch many unmanned satellites. America's Gemini Project continued in high gear as several dramatic and successful rendezvous were carried through.

The manned flights had not been without their problems. Some rendezvous attempts had had to be abandoned. One flight had had to make a premature landing because of malfunctioning controls. Nevertheless, no lives had been lost in the American program and none (despite rumors to the contrary) in the Soviet program either as 1967 opened.

The next step on the American side was the Apollo program, in which capsules containing three men were to be launched into space.

Then came disaster. On January 27, 1967, three astronauts, including White, who had been the first American to walk in space, were ground-testing the Apollo capsule in preparation for the first flight, scheduled for only a few weeks later. A fire started, somehow, and in a matter of a couple of minutes, all three were dead.

A long delay was at once necessary. The United States, to save on weight, had been using a simple oxygen atmosphere in its space capsules. This meant that if a fire did start, it would burn much more quickly and ferociously than if there were ordinary air in the capsule.

Soviet capsules, which were larger and heavier (since the

Russians used larger rockets), used ordinary air, which required bulkier equipment but was safer. Naturally, public pressure began to rise for the Americans to use ordinary air, too.

This meant new equipment, new designs, new precautions. It seemed that the new manned flights would be launched by Americans in 1967.

Nor could the Soviets find much cheer in their own program. Not long after the American disaster, in April 1967, they launched a manned capsule, their first in nearly two years. After a troubled flight, a landing was attempted and it failed. The cosmonaut, Vladimir M. Komarov, died in the crash and the Soviets found they would have to go slow, too.

Both nations continued to move forward with determination, however. In 1968, the Soviet Union sent several unmanned probes to the moon, had them circle the moon several times, then return to Earth, where they were recovered safely.

The United States then performed an even more spectacular feat. In December 1968, the probe, Apollo 8, duplicated the Soviet maneuver, but with three men aboard—Frank Borman, James Lovell, and William Anders. They left on December 21 and spent Christmas Eve, circling the moon ten times at a height of less than 70 miles. They arrived safely back on Earth on December 27.

The success of this space venture gives great grounds for hope that an actual landing on the moon will be made in 1969 and that one of the most fascinating of the science-fictional dreams of the twentieth century will come true.

When that happens, no one can tell what new knowledge and what new discoveries will be made. It seems very likely, though, that the opening horizons that will take us to the moon soon and perhaps to Mars before the twentieth century is done will help make the twenty-first century that is to come even more exciting and astonishing than the great century in which we now live.

INDEX

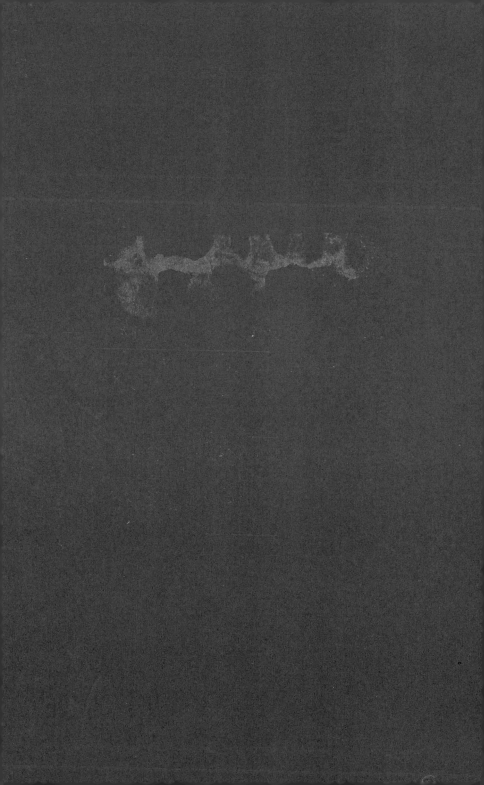